G000150297

THE LEICESTER LINE

A History of the Old Union and Grand Union Canals

INLAND WATERWAYS HISTORIES

Edited by Charles Hadfield

The Dorset & Somerset Canal. By Kenneth R. Clew
The Kennet & Avon Canal. By Kenneth R. Clew
The Leicester Line. By Philip A. Stevens
London's Lost Route to Basingstoke. By P. A. L. Vine
London's Lost Route to the Sea. By P. A. L. Vine
The Nutbrook Canal. By Peter Stevenson
The Royal Military Canal. By P. A. L. Vine
The Somersetshire Coal Canal and Railways. By Kenneth R. Clew
The Thames & Severn Canal. By Humphrey Household
The Yorkshire Ouse. By Baron F. Duckham

in preparation

The Ballinamore & Ballyconnell Canal. By Patrick Flanagan
The Birmingham Canal Navigations, vol 1. By S. R. Broadbridge
The Bude Canal. By H. Harris and M. Ellis
The Derby Canal. By Peter Stevenson
The Exeter Canal. By Kenneth R. Clew
The Forth & Clyde Canal. By Graham Matheson and D. Light
The Grand Canal of Ireland. By D. R. Delany
The Grand Junction Canal. By Alan H. Faulkner
The Great Ouse. By D. Summers
The Oxford Canal. By Hugh Compton
The Shropshire Union Canals. By H. Robinson
The Stroudwater Navigation. By M. A. Handford
The Yorkshire Derwent and Pocklington Canal. By Baron F. Duckham

Foxton Locks: the upper staircase

THE LEICESTER LINE

A HISTORY OF THE OLD UNION AND GRAND UNION CANALS

by

PHILIP A. STEVENS

With 17 plates and 6 text illustrations including maps

DAVID & CHARLES : NEWTON ABBOT

ISBN 0 7153 5536 8

Set in 11 pt Garamond, 2 pt leaded
and printed in Great Britain
by Latimer Trend & Company Limited Plymouth
for David & Charles (Publishers) Limited
South Devon House Newton Abbot Devon

Dedicated
with respect and affection
to my father
who introduced me
to the Union Canals
nearly half a century ago

Contents

Contents

Illustrations

PLATES

MAPS AND ILLUSTRATIONS IN TEXT

Preface

IT is literally true to say that I cannot remember the time when I did not know the Old Union Canal. I was born a mile away from Kilby Bridge, and before I could walk I was pushed in my perambulator along the towpath, adjustments to my clothing customary with infants being carried out in a back room of the Navigation Inn. My earliest recollections in life are of toddling beside my father along this, to me, immense waterway, plucking up courage to cross it only at Double Rail Lock—because there alone I had two handrails to cling to, and the drop to the bottom of the lock looked a very long way. In later years, the Unions remained an important factor in my life. Golden days were spent exploring their whole length, and some well loved spots became for me outdoor studies, where I read my way through sundry examinations, and indeed through a vast slice of English literature as well. As a historian, my inquiries naturally turned towards the past of these companionable waterways, and I was astonished to find that behind their placid charm lay many decades of hopeless struggle; that what for me was (and is) heart's ease had been for some heartbreak.

In the following pages, I have tried to tell this story, basing it as far as I could on what was said and done by the men who made and ran the Unions and their contemporaries. If I succeed in arousing interest in these delectable waterways which meander so unhurriedly through the heart of the grassy Shires at their most lovable, I shall feel that I have repaid a little of what they have given me, and be amply rewarded.

PHILIP A. STEVENS

Kettlebyerigge,
Kirby Bellars, Leics.

CHAPTER I

The Leicestershire & Northamptonshire Union Canal, 1792-1809

AMONG early writers on the trade potentialities of the county of Leicestershire, there was general agreement that the principal factor adversely affecting the development of the area was the lack of a good system of communication with the rest of the kingdom, and in particular the absence of a natural waterway; for the Soar, the shire's chief river, although of a fair size between Leicester and its junction with the Trent, was in its natural state quite unfitted for navigation by boats of a commercially profitable bulk. Attempts were made on more than one occasion to remedy this, but it was not until 1778 that the opening of the Soar Navigation from the Trent to Loughborough gave Leicestershire its first navigable waterway.

THE HARBOROUGH NAVIGATION

From the intense public interest aroused by this came proposals to extend this line southwards and to develop associated waterways. The obvious target was the county town, for, despite its old-established hosiery industry and a lively, progressive element in the population which was to earn it the nickname of 'Radical Leicester', the growth of the town was severely restricted by its lack of good communications. But even before Leicester was at last linked with the waterway system by the opening of the Leicester Navigation from Loughborough, consideration was being given to pushing the line of navigable water further south. There were difficulties—not least being the lack of an obvious terminal on the Soar south of Leicester; and when the project for a southward extension of the Leicester Navigation surfaced in the pages of the *Leicester Journal*, it did so as a scheme for a canal to Market Harborough, centre of the prosperous agrarian districts of south Leicestershire and north Northamptonshire.

A meeting was held at the Swan (now the Three Swans) Inn, Market Harborough, on 19 March 1792, the chair being taken by John Peach Hungerford, of Dingley Hall, Northamptonshire. Hungerford, a prominent landowner in the Harborough area, had been MP for Leicestershire between 1775 and 1790, and was a most respected and influential figure. The meeting, which was well attended, resolved that a navigation between Leicester and Harborough would be beneficial to the district, that a survey for such a canal should be undertaken by Christopher Staveley junior, and that William Jessop, now established as a leading canal engineer, in charge of the planning of the projected Leicester Navigation and Melton Mowbray Navigation apart from the greater things for which he was destined, should report on it. Individual subscriptions were to be limited to £500, and no more than £30,000 was to be subscribed at that meeting, in order to allow the landowners on the line of the intended canal to take shares if they wished. Solicitors and treasurers were appointed at both Harborough and Leicester.[1]

But already plans were afoot which were to transform the original scheme. It was known that a project was in being for a canal from London to join the Oxford Canal at Braunston, the Grand Junction Canal as it was to be called, and the gap between Harborough and the planned line of the new venture must have seemed quite narrow. At any rate, as early as 5 May 1792, rumours were appearing in the press that the Harborough canal promoters intended to carry their navigation on to form a junction with the GJ.[2] One account even pointed out the approximate area, in the vicinity of Northampton, where it was expected to do this.[3] A well-informed note in the *Leicester Journal*, commenting on the 'admirable site' for a reservoir between Saddington and Smeeton, and that the termination of the new canal would be to the west of Harborough, points out that the high level of the summit pound would be advantageous when extending into Northamptonshire,[4] though subsequently it admitted that the summit level would give difficulties.[5] Rumours also spread about other canals to link with the Harborough. One from the Leicestershire coalfield was quickly denied.[6] Another from Leicester by way of Lutterworth or Brownsover on the Oxford Canal came to nothing, support in Leicester being already heavily committed to the Harborough scheme.[7]

From Northamptonshire, too, came calls for the desired extension. It was said that some farmers in the area were sending twenty-five miles to Leicester for coal.[8] A meeting in Northampton deferred a decision on the desired extension until after the Harborough promoters' meeting, which was held at the Town Hall, Market Harborough, on 27 June 1792, with Hungerford in the chair. Having heard Staveley's report, and read a letter from Jessop, the meeting decided that the scheme was practicable and desirable, and set up a committee of thirty-four members to see it through. It was an impressive body, including not only leading landowners like Hungerford, Sir Justinian Isham of Lamport, and George Ashby of Haselbech, but also senior members of the governing body of Leicester—Aldermen Burbidge, Sutton, Clarke, and Oldham. There was no opposition to the scheme, although minor alterations were made to meet local objections, eg by Sir John Palmer, who was to raise difficulties in later years over the canal's passage through Foxton. The cost was estimated at £69,000, and, as £45,000 was to be reserved for landowners' subscriptions, this meant that no more was to be accepted from the public. The plans were to be open to landowners' inspection, and a meeting of the latter was to be called. In the meantime, a £1 call was made for preliminary expenses.[9]

But matters now changed somewhat dramatically. Hitherto, despite the rumours, the promoters had done nothing officially about the possible extension—perhaps restrained by the cautious Hungerford, for something like a coup seems to have been staged in his absence. The first committee meeting was held on 18 July 1792, at a time when Hungerford had plans to be elsewhere. He consulted several of his committee colleagues, all of whom assured him that there was nothing for the meeting but routine business; upon which he left for a tour, the chair being taken by Isham in his absence. Far from being confined to day-to-day matters, however, the issue of an extension to the Grand Junction was immediately brought up by Dr Robert Bree, a committee member who was prominent in the field of canal promotion in Leicestershire. The committee obviously could not rule on such a fundamental matter, but they did summon a general meeting to consider it.[10]

This meeting, held in Market Harborough on 6 August 1792, was extraordinary in every sense of the word.[11] The committee can hardly have anticipated the 'motley group of many hundreds of persons' who turned up—so many, that there was no room in Harborough large enough to hold them, and they had to adjourn to a field, where the chairman (Isham) took his place at the foot of an oak. They had, however, foreseen that 'canal mania' speculators would be present, and they forestalled these by insisting on share deposits being paid within seven days, though one disgruntled witness alleged that they demanded payment of £15 on the spot.[12] For the meeting agreed to the extension, which was to be regarded as separate from the original plan and subscribed for independently to the sum of £50,000 (no less than £170,000 was offered by those present at the meeting). Subscriptions were taken only from persons present, though anybody who had contributed to the survey could have three shares, whether present or not. Jessop was appointed engineer, and a survey was ordered to be made

Page 17 (*above*) LNU terminal mark, West Bridge, Leicester. Cut by the surveyor, John Parker, in 1886; (*below*) the New Cut, Leicester. Opened for traffic in 1890

Page 18 (*above*) Junction of canal and River Soar at Aylestone from the air. The canal (left channel) can be seen passing King's lock and entering the Soar just below the pack-horse bridge, a horse bridge carrying the towpath over the river at the point of junction; (*below*) King's lock, Aylestone. George King retired in 1891, aged 74, after some 50 years' service with the LNU

immediately by John Varley, whose name occurs in connection with the project for the first time.

Eleven more names were added to the committee for extension purposes. It was also reported that £31,000 had been subscribed to the original scheme, and £26,000 was being reserved for the landowners, who were to be allowed eight shares for every route mile of canal through their property. As so often in schemes of this period, vaulting ambition was at work, and retribution was ultimately to follow.

LEICESTERSHIRE & NORTHAMPTONSHIRE UNION, 1792–3

Having taken the decision to extend, the promoters had to decide the line to be adopted. The original route considered by Varley seems to have been by way of Whilton, but the committee almost at once ordered him to survey a line via Northampton to Blisworth, arguing that this would pick up trade from the region east of its course, where there was no competition, and also allow for interchange traffic with the Nene. Varley, who seems by this time to have replaced Jessop (the latter doubtless too busy with bigger projects to give his whole time to the extended Harborough scheme) as the regular engineer although there is no official record of his appointment, duly reported back to an assembly at the Swan on 3 September 1792, evidently in favour of the Northampton line, which was estimated to cost £5,000 less than that via Whilton. But he added that he thought that there was a third route, by way of Northampton to Gayton, which would be better still; and the assembly, in a hurry, told him to survey it and report to the committee on 7 September, at the same time authorising the committee to choose which of the three lines they thought best. It also laid down that the Leicester to Harborough, and the Harborough to the GJ, sections should be considered as one scheme save for purposes of subscriptions, which were to continue separate.

Varley completed his third survey in the short space of time the assembly had allowed him, and reported on it to the committee on 7 September. Whether the line adopted by the committee at this meeting was Varley's most recent survey is not known, but it seems likely that it was. An editorial in the *Leicester Journal* says that the Northamptonshire section of the line is 'above a hundred feet lower than any former which had been thought practicable, and abundant supplies of water will be found', which sounds as though it were something very recently worked out.[13] The same editorial implies that another important decision had been reached: the canal was to be broad, like the GJ—that is, constructed on such a scale as to render it capable of being used by boats of a greater beam than the seven feet or so of narrow boats.

There are indications that the committee had some trouble with the line even at this early stage. A letter appeared in the *Leicester Herald* thanking Sir John Palmer for preventing the cutting of the canal through Foxton village.[14] This caused something of a row in the paper's correspondence columns, not all the villagers, it seems, welcoming the exclusion of the canal, and it may be no coincidence that a correspondent who wrote forcefully of the parish suffering 'to gratify the caprice of a narrow-minded Individual, who has feelings only for his dear self' signed himself 'C', while a suggested alternative route not wholly abandoning the village of Foxton was brought forward by a Mr Chapman of that place.[15]

In the meantime, the committee had decided to investigate the possibilities of a cut from its own canal in Dallington, Northampton, to the river Nene. Varley duly reported on 11 October 1792 on a survey he had carried out for the purpose; and at the same time, the committee learned that the GJ had ordered its engineers, Jessop and Barnes, to determine the best place for a junction of the two canals. Arrangements were made for the apportionment of the subscriptions.[16] The demand from would-be subscribers was heavy, and shares in both the new and the Old Harborough schemes soon rose to a premium.[17] A project for an independent canal from the Harborough scheme to Uppingham had to be suspended for the time being, as there was not time to get plans prepared for the next Parliamentary session, but, far from being abandoned, an extension to Stamford was talked of.[18]

But the committee was now experiencing the usual trouble with landowners—whose reluctance to subscribe for the shares offered to them in proportion to the distance the canal was to run through their lands caused more than one extension of the period during which these were reserved for them. Some made separate deals—like the Earl of Harborough, who got a guarantee of £18 for tolls on carts, etc, at that town which he might lose by the coming of the canal. The Earl and Countess of Denbigh, with whom the company was to have trouble in the near future, got clauses put into the Bill safeguarding their property at Newton Harcourt and Wistow. However, landowners' opposition does not seem to have been bitter, and even the Denbighs in the end applied for more shares than they were entitled to.

During this period of bargaining with the squires, the committee had been settling the line for which it was to apply for an Act. Varley and Staveley submitted their final plans to the committee on 9 November 1792, and were instructed to send them on to Jessop for his approval or amendment, and then to deposit them with the Clerks of the Peace for Leicestershire and Northamptonshire. At some stage between 14 October, when the parliamentary notice relating to this project still announced its intention of making the canal as far as the GJ at Gayton, and 11 November, when the plans were deposited, the decision had been taken not to make the Northampton–Gayton section, but to join at the former place a branch made by the GJ from the latter. Possibly it was made at Jessop's suggestion when Varley brought the plans along, for the line of the GJ branch at Northampton is very roughly sketched in, in contrast to the beautiful drawing-office style of the main body of the plan.

The committee also settled the style of the concern, since 'Harborough Navigation' was obviously no longer suitable. No doubt several names were suggested—there is a hint that one may have been 'Grand Union'—but the final choice, first appearing in full publicly on 7 December 1792, was that by which the company was to be known for over a hundred years —'The Leicestershire & Northamptonshire Union Canal'.[19]

THE PASSAGE OF THE ACT (1792–3)

Little occurred to disturb the smooth passage of the Bill through Parliament. The committee was not happy about the landowners' continuing backwardness in subscribing, and extended the period for them to do so yet again; and the townsfolk of Market Harborough took umbrage at the insertion of a clause into the Bill allowing the proposed canal from Uppingham to make a junction with the LNU, and at a resolution from Kettering favouring a canal to link that town with the latter—selfishly arguing that Harborough would lose the benefits it expected from its position as the sole centre for canal traffic in the region. The committee refused to oblige by amending the Bill, pointing out that Harborough could oppose these matters when the occasion arose. These were trifles; but the committee seems to have taken fright at the unexpected appearance of an anonymous pamphlet attacking the scheme. This argued that the projected canal was unnecessary, since as soon as the GJ was opened, one of the LNU's stated aims—to open up a trade between London on the one hand and Liverpool and Hull on the other—would be achieved, by way of Braunston, Fazeley, and the Trent & Mersey Canal. Northampton would be better served by the Staffordshire–Warwickshire coalfield (and by the West Leicestershire coalfield if the Ashby Canal project came to anything) than by Derbyshire. The corn trade from Northamptonshire, of which much had been made in canal propaganda, fluctuated greatly from season to season, and indeed was less than formerly, since so much of the arable in the county had been enclosed and turned over to pasture. Jessop was quoted as saying that without the LNU, the GJ's Northampton branch would be unprofitable, but the writer dismisses this with the comment that every branch could not be expected to be profitable in itself—the concern must be judged as a whole; even without the LNU, the GJ's Northampton branch would bring a lot of traffic on to its main line. Furthermore, water supply on the LNU would be very difficult, as much of the country through which it intended to pass often could not provide enough water even for the cattle which grazed there; and when the canal was low, 'exhalations of a pernicious tendency' would damage the health of the residents, especially in a southwest wind. The line itself came in for criticism, and Jessop was blamed for not looking at 'the Line recommended and surveyed by Mr. Ringrose' which apparently would have made Braunston the junction of the LNU and GJ.[20]

The committee (now in London to follow the progress of the Bill), was sufficiently worried to ask Jessop to answer the pamphlet, copies of his reply to be sent to 'such Gentlemen as are likely to attend to the Reasons'. Presumably in consequence of this, a long advertisement appeared in the *Northampton Mercury*, answering the pamphlet point by point.[21] It is not signed, but the kindliness characteristic of Jessop, most attractive character of all our early engineers, seems to be present throughout—eg he supposes that 'the Author's Opinion has rather been biassed by Misinformation that from any invidious Motive', a charitable view not many of his contemporaries would have taken. The writer, moreover, does not poke fun at his opponent's absurd statement that the canal would injure the turnpike roads by putting more traffic on them, leaving that argument to sink under the weight of its own silliness, but corrects the pamphlet's misstatements, some of which were gross—the estimate for the Harborough branch, for instance, is said to be £30,000, whereas it was in fact £7,007. Whether due to the reply or not, such opposition as there was to the Bill dwindled, until on 2 March 1793, the *Leicester Herald* reported that all objections were removed;[22] while on 16 March, it was being spoken of as certain to succeed.[23] On 28 March, the Lords Committee on Unopposed Private Bills examined it, Jessop being called on to prove the scheme's practicability and desirability, and Staveley the survey.[24] The committee reported it, having first exercised its authority by deleting 'aforesaid' from clause 113. The Royal Assent was given on 30 April 1793, and the Leicestershire & Northamptonshire Union Canal Company was in being.

THE ACT, 1793

The company's Act of 30 April 1793 (33 Geo III, c 98) authorised it to make the river Soar navigable from the Leicester Navigation, 'now making', near West Bridge, Leicester, to near Aylestone Bridge, and to make thence a canal to the Nene at Northampton, and to a branch from the GJ in Hardingstone parish. It incorporated 576 named individuals into a company for this purpose. The list is not a brilliant one—only five peers (all with Leicestershire connections and none with extensive possessions on the line of the canal), and two baronets; but it contained some very solid local names, of leaders in the public (Bankart, Burbidge, Clarke, Coltman) and professional (Mansfield, Bosworth, Inkersole) life of the town and county of Leicester.

The authorised line began just north of the West Bridge in Leicester, making an end-on junction with the Leicester Navigation, and deviated almost at once from the Soar to avoid the Castle Mill. The first major cut, however, came at about a quarter of a mile south of the West Bridge, to pass another—the Swans—Mill. After this, the line followed the Soar, with more cuts to get round St Mary's and Aylestone Mills and a minor straightening, to the old pack-horse bridge at Aylestone, near which the river was left altogether in favour of an artificial canal. This nevertheless stuck closely to the course of the Soar until, near Whetstone, it turned east to follow the river Sence, a tributary of the Soar which joined that river here. It continued to follow the Sence, never more than a few hundred yards away, and usually much closer, until it reached the watershed between Saddington and Fleckney. It crossed this by a 45 chain tunnel, and continued over the Smeeton valley (a reservoir had been talked of in this area, but does not appear on the plan), until the rising ground near Foxton necessitated another tunnel, 48 chains long, to carry the line into the Welland valley. Beyond this tunnel, there was a junction, the branch to Harborough going off to the east and terminating alongside the Leicester to Harborough turnpike road on the site of the present basin, while the main line to Northampton headed westwa To cross the broad Welland valley, the latter had to take a very circuitous course, describing nearly three-quarters of a circle around Marston Trussell before ascending the southern slopes near East Farndon, and finally breaking out of the valley by a 13 chain tunnel near Great Oxendon. This took it into the valley of the Oxendon brook, at the crossing of which there was to be a reservoir. The fourth and last tunnel (45 chains) took the canal into the valley of one of the streams which formed the Northern River, a branch of the Nene. The canal followed this to Dallington, where it joined the Northern River for the short final stretch before dividing into two, one channel going to the junction of the GJ branch and the Nene at Far Coton, the other rejoining the Northern River near the latter's confluence with the main channel of the Nene. The total length of the line from Leicester to the junction with the GJ branch was given as 43 miles 5 furlongs 7 chains 97 links, and the Market Harborough branch as 3 miles 6 furlongs 8 chains 38 links. There was a rise of 160ft from West Bridge to the pound in which Saddington tunnel was to be cut, achieved by twenty-three locks. Thence the canal (including the Harborough branch) was level to near Great Oxendon, where a flight of locks was to raise it 50ft to its summit level in some 250yd. The summit pound, just under 5 miles long, ended near Maidwell, whence the final 12½ miles descended 197ft.

The company was authorised to take water from watercourses found during the making of the canal, within defined limits; and to make reservoirs—but not in any place not so designated on the plan certified by the Speaker of the House of Commons without the consent of the landowners (as noted above, the intended reservoir near Saddington failed to get on to the plan). The canal was to be made as far as possible from Maidwell Hall (which belonged to Hungerford, the company's chairman!) and was not to be nearer than 440yd to Kelmarsh Hall; its course through Glen Parva was likewise strictly controlled. There are clauses protecting the owners from possible loss of water from their streams in Wistow, Kelmarsh, the Oxendons, and Coton Mill, Northampton. The towpath in Wistow must be on the side opposite Wistow Hall, unless the Countess of Denbigh agrees otherwise. The width of the canal, with towpath and fences, is not to exceed 20yd except at wharves, etc, or where the canal is more than 5ft above or below the natural surface level, or at winding holes. As the canal would cut across the path to St Mary's Mill, the company was either to buy the mill or build a bridge, at the option of its owner. The usual restrictions on the company, orders relating to the appointment of commissioners, etc, were included in the Act's 91 pages.

To pay for all this, the company was empowered to raise a capital of not more than £200,000 in £100 shares. If this were insufficient, a further sum of up to £100,000 could be raised among the proprietors, or by the admission of new subscribers, or in any manner the company should think proper, including mortage of the undertaking. Every subscriber to the share capital was to have, at assemblies, one vote for every share held, up to a maximum of ten. The appointment of clerks, treasurers, and toll collectors was to be in the hands of the General Assembly, but the day to day running was entrusted to a General Committee of thirteen persons, each holding a minimum of one share in the company, the quorum being five, and such other committees of seven (quorum three) as the assembly appointed. The General Committee was required to keep minutes of its proceedings and accounts of its financial transactions, and to report to the General Assembly half-yearly.

In return for this, the company was authorised to collect tolls at the following rates:

Coal and coke—2½d per ton per mile; maximum 5s (25p) per ton.
Lime, manure, dung, limestone—1½d per ton per mile; maximum 2s 6d (12½p) per ton.
Cattle, sheep, swine, and other animals, stone, bricks, tiles, slates, ironstone, pig iron—2d per ton per mile.
All other goods—3d per ton per mile.

Fractions of a mile were to be taken to the nearest mile above; fractions of a ton to the nearest quarter ton above. Soldiers on duty bound and naval and military supplies were exempted from toll, as was material for repairing public roads, and fertilisers for owners of lands adjoining the canal, when water was running to waste over the weirs.

Hours during which traffic was permitted were from 7am to 5pm from November to February; 5am to 7pm in March–April and September–October; and 4am to 9pm between May and August. Boats less than 60ft long and 12ft wide were not to be allowed through the locks without the company's consent unless water were running over the waste weirs above the locks. The company was to buy enough land above the tunnels to make horse roads. The sides of the canal were to be puddled to prevent leakage in the lands of certain named individuals in Newton Harcourt, Great Glenn, Kibworth Beauchamp, the Oxendons, Saddington, and Lubenham. Time for cutting the canal through the lands of the Countess of Denbigh was optimistically limited to twelve months after the beginning of the cutting, and in the case of William Pares, even more so to six months.

The traffic regulation section of the Act orders that all boats shall have their number and the name of the master, with his address, in 3in high white letters on them, and indications in metal to show the depth at various ladings; they must also be gauged by the company's servants when required, but not more than three times a year. Owners of lands alongside the canal may put pleasure craft on it free of toll, but if they wish to pass a lock when water is not running to waste, they must pay as for 10 tons load.

Looking to the future, the Act authorised the junction with the LNU of the intended canal from Uppingham, and, perhaps with the Kettering project in mind, a clause empowers the company to apply to Parliament for sanction to make branches on a majority vote of the proprietors.

The powers thus granted by the Act were considerable, and the restrictions not too crippling. It remained now for the youthful company to carry them out.

CONSTRUCTION BEGINS (1793–4)

The company held its first General Assembly at the Bell Inn, Market Harborough, on 1 May 1793, the chief business being to elect the General Committee and the clerk.[25] In the latter case, the dualism which for some years was to characterise the LNU appeared, for clerks were appointed at both Leicester (John Edward Carter and John Heyrick) and Harborough (George Wartnaby). In the same way, the second General Assembly on 6 May 1793, at the Swans, elected treasurers in Leicester (Bentley & Buxton) as well as at Harborough (Bosworth & Inkersole).[26] It is possible that the dissension which was to plague the company during the next few years appeared in connection with these appointments, for a notice was issued by Bosworth & Inkersole thanking their supporters for, it seems, preventing a motion hostile to them from being put to the vote at the first General Assembly.[27]

An important action taken by the second General Assembly was the appointment of a committee for managing the construction of the Leicester end of the line (hereinafter to be referred to as the Leicester Committee). A similar body was set up for the Northampton end, but no record survives of its meetings, if indeed it held any, for nothing was to come of this part of the scheme. The Leicester Committee was a powerful body composed mainly of senior members of the magistracy of the town: Aldermen Clarke, Burbidge, Oldham, and Gregory, with the Rev George Foster, Samuel Clarke, and John Nichols. The two last named were members of the town council, both subsquently becoming aldermen, and Nichols alone of the six corporation members on the committee never held the office of Mayor of Leicester.[28] The town was thus powerfully if unofficially represented. The Leicester Committee served the company well, meeting weekly and sometimes more often—as in August 1793, when it met on six of the seven first days of the month; on two occasions it met at the extraordinary time of 6am on West Bridge. By virtue of their position in the public life of the town, the members were no doubt accustomed to getting their own way, and they dealt summarily with opposition: at various times, they rebuked sharply the company's servants (for not producing information fast enough), the General Committee (for requesting the Leicester Committee to attend one of its meetings at Harborough, which it declined to do), and even the body of proprietors (for attending assemblies for the sole purpose of pocketing and walking off with the bottles of wine the company provided for their refreshment). Only when it tackled the press did the committee come off second best: it quarrelled with Phillips, editor of the *Leicester Herald*, a strong supporter of the scheme, whose chief offence seems to have been an excess of zeal in inserting advertisements more often than ordered. The committee indignantly cancelled all the company's advertising in the *Herald*, thereby making an enemy. The first fruits of this tactless action appeared almost at once, an editorial in the *Herald* calling on canal subscribers to resist excessive calls, and to suspend some schemes—the LNU was clearly meant—until better times.[29] From this time on, the *Herald* was a constant critic of the venture, and its influence must have encouraged the growth of dissension which soon appeared.

No record is preserved of the formal appointment of an engineer to take charge of construction. In view of the fact that payments were authorised in the early minutes of the Leicester

Committee to 'the Engineers' jointly on equal terms, it seems that Varley and Staveley were appointed jointly, though Varley was regarded as the senior, being asked to lay down a programme for the first year's work (he recommended against beginning any work at the Northampton end for the time being).[30] Varley himself seems to have had some doubts about his appointment, which appears only to have been until May 1794, for he told the Leicester Committee in November 1793 that he had the offer of a job nearer his family in Yorkshire, and wanted to know whether it was intended to engage him full time after the expiry of his present term. The committee felt that the enterprise could not do without him, and said it would recommend that he be retained, which he duly was. In view of subsequent events—and of Varley's connection with unsatisfactory work elsewhere[31]—perhaps it would have been better advised to let him go. Staveley's connection with the LNU probably ended about July 1794.

In accordance with Varley's report, work began at the Leicester end, with the taking down and partial rebuilding of the West Bridge, during which time this structure, which carried one of the main roads into the town, was closed to traffic. The closure was from 8 July to 27 July 1793, to the indignation of those whose livelihood depended on the road, and the company had to pay £3 4s (£3.20) to the lessee of the Narborough turnpike gate in compensation for loss of tolls. To offset this, the town council gave the company a piece of land by the bridge, and offered £20 if the whole bridge were rebuilt.[32] The committee was also experiencing the minor irritations inseparable from the enterprise. Various citizens had encroached on the land designated for the company at West Bridge, and the committee had to accompany the engineer to mark the bounds afresh. The millers at Abbey, North, and Castle Mills proved as uncooperative in regulating their water supplies as their fellows elsewhere often were, and the committee had to threaten action.

Meanwhile, the committee was preoccupied with securing

workmen and materials to get the scheme under way. It advertised for bricklayers (who could tender for a number of locks or bridges), brickmakers—urgently needed—and 'diggers'.[33] It was successful as regards bricklayers—work was begun on Castle Mill lock in July, and finished at the end of November.[34] Labourers, too, were to be found, and by December at least 300 of them were at work.[35] Early in the new year, contracts were let for four locks each to James Rouse of Leicester and John Allen and Thomas Davis of Enderby, with an unspecified number of locks and bridges to John Insele and Smith & Bradley. Procuring bricks gave more trouble. The Leicester Committee had decided, lacking advice from Staveley, who did not trouble to attend the second meeting of the committee when the matter was discussed, to order as many as possible locally, and hopefully asked for 'two or three persons' to tender for the bricks the company needed. The small quantities offered must have been a disappointment. Figures mentioned are 10,000 and 18,000 bricks, and from payments made it is clear that these were the usual consignments. And some of the bricks were far from satisfactory—indeed, the committee closed its account with Mansfield of Aylestone, expressing itself with some asperity about the conduct of Staveley (again absent) in engaging such a workman. It was at last successful in placing a large contract at the end of November 1793, when Goodman & Mitchell undertook to make 3 millions and Dilks 1 million. Other contracts for 800,000 followed. Greater numbers had also reduced prices: the company paid up to £1 9s 6d (£1.47½) per thousand in its earlier agreements, while those contracted for in late 1793 were supplied at prices ranging from 9s to 9s 3d (45p to 46p) per thousand.

By the end of November 1793, the Leicester section was complete enough for constructional materials to be boated up it, and water was 'breast high' in the new cut at Aylestone.[36] But a rift was developing within the company. Maybe it dated from the transformation of the Harborough Navigation into the Union Canal. It must certainly have been accentuated by the rise in prices of goods and labour due to the war with France, for the company had already experienced a labour dispute serious enough to cause the authorities to hold troops in readiness to quell riots.[37] The first intimation of trouble was the appearance of a notice in the *Herald* summoning an unofficial meeting of LNU proprietors on 11 February 1794, to consider suspending constructional activities.[38] At the meeting, a majority of those present resolved that a Special General Meeting of the company should be requested to discuss calling a halt to work upon the canal.[39] The General Committee thereupon took space in the *Leicester Journal* to inform the public that there was no intention of stopping work.[40] It was backed up by the *Journal*, which took up the cudgels for the congenial task of belabouring its loathed journalistic rival—referring to the fainthearted proprietors anxious to give up as 'Harborough lame ducks'.[41] The *Herald* retaliated by attempting to shake shareholders' confidence by asserting that the company had begun 'over 100' actions against defaulting proprietors. In reply, the committee merely ordered a fresh call of £5 per cent, making £15 per cent in all, and gave backsliders until 18 March 1794 to pay up.[42] It was, however, worried: coal for burning bricks at Aylestone was in such short supply that it planned to appeal to the Leicester Navigation and the Leicestershire coalowners, hoping to persuade the latter to allow Derbyshire coal to pass along the navigation for LNU use, despite the clause in the Leicester Navigation's Act forbidding it to handle Derbyshire coal until Leicestershire coal could compete by way of the Forest Line from the Leicestershire coalfield to Loughborough. Moreover, Varley had reached the end of the land the company had in hand, and workmen were being laid off and were leaving. But the committee put on a bold front, and, when the *Herald* carried a notice asking proprietors wishing to have the construction of the canal stopped at the crossing of the turnpike road from Leicester to Welford, to attend the General Assembly in May, and bring the matter up, it reiterated in the *Journal* that it did not intend to give up, and that the majority of shareholders supported this line.[43] Events proved it right; for, if suspension were indeed discussed at the General Assembly on 5 May 1794, no resolution in favour of it was passed.[44] Perhaps the committee had cleverly forestalled criticism: on 30 April 1794, it ordered that an advertisement for tenders for supplying lime at Aylestone should be published, 'and giving notice that the Leicestershire Union Canals are open so far'.[45]

THE COMPANY IN DIFFICULTIES (1794–97)

The committee had thus overcome the opposition in the company's own ranks, but it was evidently concerned about the financing of the construction of the works—15 per cent of the capital had been called up and only a few miles of waterway were open or under construction; and all the most expensive engineering works lay ahead of the company, with prices rising rapidly. Bricks, for instance, which they had once got for as little as 9s (45p) per thousand had now risen to £1 11s (£1.55). It therefore announced its recommendation that application be made for an Act to deviate the line from Gumley to Great Bowden.[46] The matter, which arose from a wish to avoid the planned tunnel at Foxton, was deliberated at the General Assembly on 3 November 1794, when it was decided to get Robert Whitworth to survey the suggested deviation and report on it in December. In due course, Whitworth recommended the abandonment of the 'great Tunnel' at Foxton in favour of a line through the village, to join the authorised line at Market Harborough, thus making the branch part of the main line, and a Special General Assembly was summoned at Harborough on 15 December 1794 to discuss this.[47] It was, however, dramatically prevented from doing so. As soon as Hungerford took the chair, Sir John Palmer, the leading landowner at Foxton, entered and apologising for intruding, as he was not a shareholder, reminded the assembled shareholders that he had been promised when the scheme was first promoted that the canal should not be taken through the village. Despite efforts to dissuade him, he clung to this, and eventually the meeting was forced to yield, the intended deviation being abandoned.[48]

Despite this setback, matters at the Leicester end were progressing reasonably well. On 28 October 1794, the arrival of the first coal boats in Leicester along the Leicester Navigation, signalling the long-awaited commencement of the trade in waterborne coal from Derbyshire, was greeted with great rejoicing, and the LNU (which was duly mentioned in an interminable ode orated by the poet at the celebrations as a potential 'blessing to mankind') added its own contribution to the gaiety by extending its opened line as far as Blaby, a coal boat proceeding thither.[49]

The Leicester Committee was still concerned with the shortage of land the company had in hand, and, in dealing with Lady Denbigh for her lands in Newton Harcourt and Wistow, which the engineers desperately needed, for once called for help, asking Hungerford to see her about them. Whether because of Hungerford's social position and prestige, or his persuasiveness, or because the committee agreed to pay whatever price the valuer put on the land before it even heard it, the land seems to have been made over to the company, for soon after this, the committee turned its attention to a proposed deviation in Smeeton Westerby and Saddington, which was agreed to. Navvies were undoubtedly at work in the Newton Harcourt and Saddington area at the end of March 1795, for a party of 'at least threescore' took part in the celebrated riots which began with the arrest of two drunken navvies for assault in a Kibworth shop, and their subsequent 'rescue' by their comrades from an escort of some forty fencibles taking them to Leicester for trial on 30 March 1795. The Leicester magistrates immediately despatched the Loyal Leicester Volunteer Infantry, who left in such haste that their ammunition had to be sent after them, followed by the Volunteer Cavalry. The latter went to Newton Harcourt, where, at the local inn, they arrested 'four of the most desperate of the rioters', though not, apparently, the men

Page 35 (*above*) Kilby Bridge. The white building in the centre of the rise in the background was the surveyor's house; (*below*) Sence aqueduct, Great Glenn

Page 36 (*above*) Saddington tunnel, north portal; (*below*) aqueduct over footpath, Smeeton Westerby

whose liberation had begun the whole affair. Next day, the cavalry made another sortie, and brought in a further nine prisoners, including 'Red Jack' and 'Northamptonshire Tom' who had 'terrorised every county they have resided in'.[50] Nine of the prisoners were acquitted, two were fined (they were unable to pay the stiff fines of £40 and £50 imposed, and stayed in gaol) and the other two were given the option of joining the navy or going to gaol, which recalls Dr Johnson's expressed preference for the second of these two evils.

Riots or no, the committee was busy developing trade on the canal. A wharfinger was appointed at Blaby, and a house built for him. The same was done at Kilby Bridge, the wharfinger, William Bellamy, being paid 10s (50p) per week. Lady Denbigh's agent was approached concerning a wharf at Great Glenn. To get business started, arrangements were made for the delivery of fifteen boatloads of coal at Kilby Wharf.

With the line advancing slowly southwards, the committee came up against the first of the major engineering works, the tunnel near Saddington. On 25 June 1795, it examined tenders, and let the first 180yd to James Gladwell, to be completed by 25 December. On 2 July, it increased this by a further 230yd, completion date to be 25 March 1796, with a five-guinea bonus to Gladwell over the (unspecified) contract price if he finished it by 25 February. At the same time, the remaining 470yd at the southern end were let to Thomas Packer Batchelor and Robert Biggs. However, this was cancelled on 16 July, as they could not find sufficient surety. What happened about the letting of the contract after this is obscure. At the end of the year, Valentine Harrison, Henry Ludlam, and Thomas Walker had been working on the tunnel long enough to get themselves into financial difficulties, a fourth contractor, Thomas Hill, had run away from his work rather than face the monetary troubles it had led him into, another, Joseph Parkin, seems to have taken over from Walker, while in February 1796, still another, Peter Tipping, was called in to complete certain parts of the tunnel. In these circumstances, it is likely that trouble would have arisen over the tunnel even if Varley had carried out his duties more conscientiously than he appears to have done.

But by now it must have been clear to the Leicester Committee that the company's finances were not going to support the execution of the whole scheme. A further call, due on 21 September 1795, had brought the total called-up capital to 45 per cent, and the major engineering obstacles of the line had not even been reached. So, on 15 October 1795, the committee ordered that no further work should be begun beyond Debdale, near the village of Gumley, without its 'particular order'.[51] A meeting of proprietors called to support this was told that arrears on calls amounted to no less than £13,000, and a limit of 10 per cent per annum was placed on future calls.[52]

The committee also reviewed the work on the tunnel. John Clarke was severely rebuked for his lack of progress on the deep cutting east of it, while in the tunnel itself, Harrison, Ludlam, and Walker were all deeply in the company's debt (this was why Hill had bolted), and worked very slowly. Moved by this to examine the contracts, the committee found that contractors' misconduct had cost the company £400, and ordered that no more contracts should be let without its consent. To add to its troubles, the cutting west of the tunnel fell in, and it impatiently overruled the engineer's suggestion of a brick wall instead. Probably by now it had begun to distrust Varley, for it ordered him in future to report to each committee meeting the progress made on the tunnel. The order had to be repeated on 5 May, when 347yd of the tunnel had been completed.

Still worse was in store. On 6 July 1796, the committee was informed that John Fletcher, who had been appointed clerk to the company in July 1795 and had taken over the functions previously performed by Staveley, had found the tunnel to be out of straight.[53] This was in flat contradiction to a report by Varley on 11 February. The committee ordered the matter to be investigated at once, and Varley offered to pay the expenses of rectifying any error found to be due to faulty engineering.

One of the committee members, Alderman William Oldham, a Leicester architect and builder of repute, having inspected the tunnel and said that it was indeed not straight, James Barnes, one of the GJ's engineers, was called in, and his report was presented to the committee on 10 August 1796.[54] It included a visual aid in the form of a paper cut-out representing a boat of the type Barnes assumed would use the LNU, and this could be propelled along a sketch depicting the tunnel as it was being built, so that the committee members could see for themselves that such a boat would stick in several places. He blamed Varley, for neglecting the proper measures in laying out the line of the tunnel. The brickwork he praised, though he found that the contractors were needlessly extravagant in the use of bricks. In his concluding paragraph—the sting in the tail—he comments caustically on the 'differences' existing between the company's servants, winding up '. . . were they to exert themselves as much to serve the Concern as they do to injure each other, it might be more to the Company's Advantage'. He does not specify individuals, but it is difficult to believe that Varley and Fletcher can have been on good terms now. Presumably Varley paid for the necessary alterations; there is no record of this, or of any instructions the committee may have issued. All that is recorded is that the tunnel made quite good progress—627yd completed by 24 August; 661yd by 7 September; 750yd by 5 October; 759yd by 19 October (Varley had laid down 20yd per week as a fair average rate of construction).

The committee henceforth kept a much closer watch on activities during the final stages of the canal's completion to Debdale. On 14 December 1796, it handed over the construction of the entire section from the tunnel to Debdale to Fletcher, no doubt regarding him as a trustworthy servant since the affair of the tunnel defects. The price was £902 14s 6d (£902.72½p) and he retained the general supervision of the works as well. Shortly after, land was bought for the basin at Debdale.[55] Having done this, the committee began to pave the way—almost literally—for development by making an agreement with the Surveyor of the Highways of the area in which the intended wharf was to be situated, under which it was to supply gravel for the roads to the wharf, and the surveyor was to provide a labour force of at least four men to spread it to a width of 5yd and a depth of 20in at the middle, 15in at the sides, on the roads concerned.

The tunnel was virtually completed by 22 February, when it was ordered that water should not be let into it until Oldham had inspected it and approved. The exact date on which it was opened is unrecorded, but Debdale wharf was declared open for public traffic on 7 April 1797, and it is unlikely that the tunnel was opened long before then. James Gibson, owner of the first boat to pass through, was given his toll money back to mark the event. It is not said what his cargo was; perhaps the Derbyshire coal which was soon being advertised for sale at Debdale wharf, at 11d per cwt.[56]

The committee, happy in the knowledge that part at least of its task was done, sent Fletcher's books back to him, with a request for his statement of outstanding bills so that the company could clear off its debts and review its finances. And so, with a terminus in the depths of the countryside, 4 miles from Market Harborough and 2 miles from the nearest village, the LNU settled down to take stock of its position, and to recruit its strength for a fresh advance.

EXTENSION AND ABANDONED HOPES (1797–1809)

For some months, the Leicester Committee was occupied in tidying up loose ends. The company's formal connection with Varley ended on 2 November 1797, but he continued to act as consultant, charging £1 11s 6d (£1.57½) per day plus expenses. His help was needed, for Fletcher had failed to complete his contract, and Varley took it over, being paid £60, the company finding and paying workmen. Fletcher was paid £138 9s (£138.45) and left the LNU scene. Orders were given that Thomas Clarke, the toll collector in Leicester, should be sent

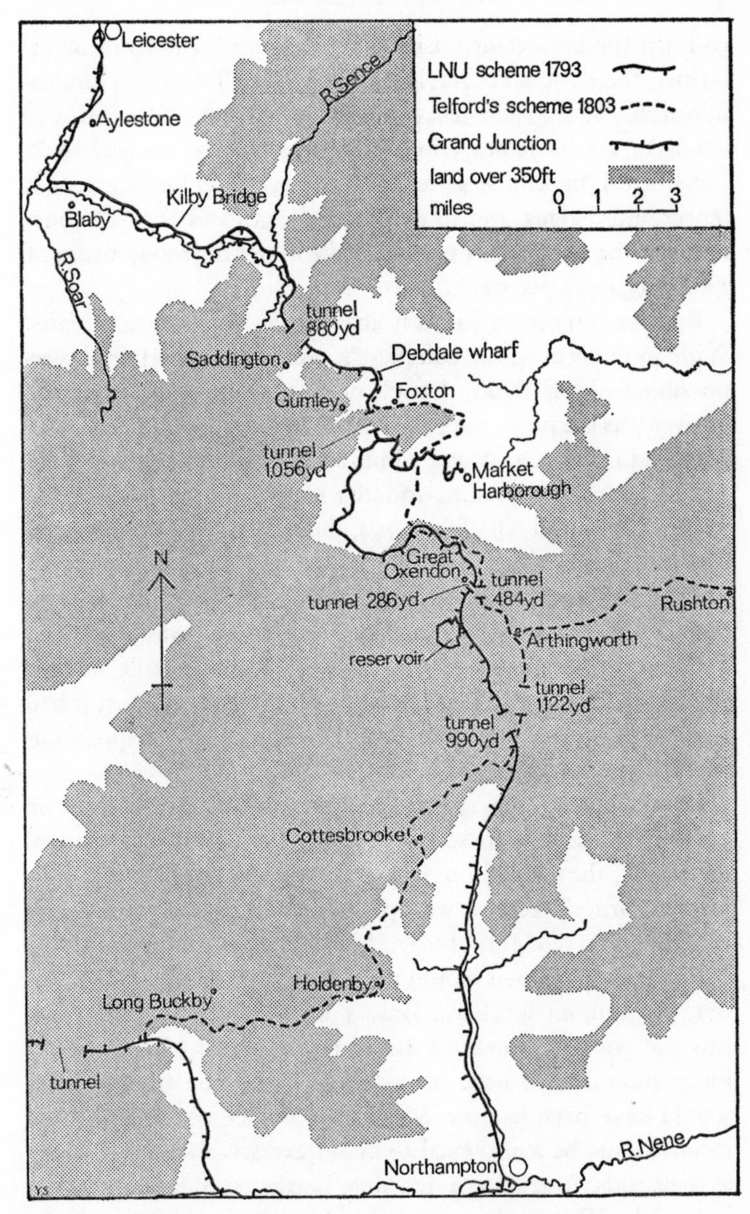

FIGURE 1. Map of LNU, 1793 and associated schemes

to learn the important business of gauging boats from Swinburne, the Leicester Navigation's toll collector at Loughborough. The maintenance of the works of the canal was handed over to James Gibson, who undertook to find lockkeepers, oil the 'cloughs', regulate the water, and look after the fences and hedges, and to deliver messages and perform journeys for the company. For all this, he asked the modest sum of £2 15s (£2.75) per week.

But the committee had not abandoned the extension plans. With 40 per cent of the company's capital not called up, it was possible to look ahead, though no doubt the chief immediate anxiety was the projected reservoir at Saddington, which Varley surveyed in 1797, as it was admitted in August 1797 that trade would be poor for some months owing to the shortage of water. Not until 29 July 1799, however, did the General Assembly authorise the raising of money 'for the purpose of making a Reservoir at Gumley and Saddington', whereupon the committee made a £1 per cent call.[57] Land was bought in Saddington parish on 20 May 1800.[58] The reservoir was no doubt made immediately after this—at any rate, in 1805, it had been there long enough for doubts as to its safety, happily unfounded, to have arisen.

Following up the question of extension, the committee decided to seek the best advice, and, backed by the General Assembly, they called on James Barnes to report on the subject.[59] Barnes's report was presented to a Special General Assembly on 26 July 1802. He began by condemning the parliamentary line—it would need puddling virtually throughout, the summit level was only 5 miles long and would not provide enough water for the expected trade (the Oxendon locks should have been placed at Foxton—the summit level would have been lengthened and the tunnel avoided) and the tunnels must be lengthened to avoid excessively deep cuttings at their ends. In seeking a new line, Barnes considered the trade potential of Birmingham as well as London, and his line therefore brought the canal 22½ miles nearer the former. It approximated to the authorised line for the first mile or so, gaining height by five locks, but at Foxton it left it completely, climbing Foxton hill by six locks and heading for the GJ near Norton, descending into it by seven locks. The chief works would be tunnels at Husbands Bosworth and Crick, 1,122 and 1,430yd respectively. The Harborough branch would leave the main line at the foot of Foxton locks, pass through Foxton village, where it would be 'an ornament to the place' (so much for Sir John Palmer!), wind around the high ground by way of Great Bowden, to end in 'Round Hill Close', half a mile from Harborough. The line to the GJ would be 11½ miles shorter than the authorised line to Gayton, and involved 184yd less tunnelling. Barnes's estimate, based on a depth of 5ft of water (5ft 6in in the summit pound) and a width of 42ft at the top, 27ft at the bottom (43ft 6in and 27ft on the summit) was £146,960. Revenue from trade he believed would be £46,787 10s (£46,787.50).[60]

Barnes's work was conscientiously done, and was to have its effect in the future, though not on the LNU. But for some reason, the proprietors do not seem to have been satisfied, for on 4 January 1803, the committee asked no less a personage than Thomas Telford to carry out the same task. In his report, dated 23 May 1803, Telford agreed with Barnes about the deficiencies of the parliamentary line.[61] But he also criticised Barnes's line—it ran too far west, and was too high, so that it would be expensive to maintain (because it had many locks to make and keep up) and lay above the springs which should have fed it. He admitted that a line was difficult to find anywhere in this hilly district, but, as he had ranged far to the east, he had discovered one. This line followed more or less the route of Barnes's Harborough branch, but continued southwards, to the west of the town, crossing the Welland Valley on a lofty embankment to save 7 miles on the parliamentary line, and passing via East Farndon and Oxendon to Arthingworth, where a 6 mile branch went off to Rushton. The main line continued by way of Maidwell, Cottesbrooke, Creaton, and

Holdenby, to join the GJ near Buckby wharf. The mileage, including the branch, was 42 miles. There were only 23ft of lockage, and the summit pound, 31 miles long, would be well supplied with waste water, as the line was 54ft lower than Barnes's. There would be two tunnels, 484yd and 1,122yd respectively. The total cost would be £247,692, and estimated revenue£41,893—promising a 15 per cent return on capital.

Perhaps it was this last prospect which induced the proprietors to adopt Telford's report on 20 June 1803.[62] On the other hand, it may have been that the General Assembly noted that Harborough lay on Telford's main line, so that his scheme would bring in revenue much sooner than Barnes's, unless they delayed making the latter's main line to construct the branch first, when they would have had serious difficulties with the water supply. The shareholders were understandably reluctant to add to their costs by applying to Parliament for powers to make the line if they could get them otherwise, and they first tried to persuade the commissioners appointed under their Act to permit them to deviate their line to cover the stretch they intended to make first, from Debdale to the east side of the turnpike road from Leicester to Harborough just north of the latter place.[63] Having no success there, the company duly announced its intention of applying for an Act to deviate this section of the line, but added that its ultimate aim was to complete the rest of the line according to the parliamentary plan, which, if meant literally, involved abandoning Telford's scheme and reverting to that of 1792.[64] In anticipation, a £4 per cent call was made.[65]

Of the landowners, 21 agreed, 9 dissented, and 7 were neutral to the new plan. (Sir John Palmer was among those assenting, though the line neatly divided the upper half of Foxton from the lower.) The line was surveyed by John Howell, and his estimate for construction, including the land, was £15,421 10s 6d (£15,421.52½).[66] Speaking for the LNU before the Lords Committee, Wartnaby said that the company had spent £170,000 and expected to have to find another

£100,000 to reach the GJ at Long Buckby (which implies that it still had Telford's route in mind, though if so, it had slashed his estimate). LNU shares, on which £70 had been paid, now stood at £20.[67] Despite this gloomy prospect, the Bill was passed, and the Royal Assent given on 27 June 1805 (45 Geo III, c 71). This authorised the deviation of the line via Foxton and Great Bowden to Market Harborough, terminating west of the turnpike road, and included safe-guards to protect Foxton.[68] There were no clauses authorising the raising of money; as the estimate was so low, and the company's capital by no means fully called up, there was no apparent reason for them.

On Telford's advice, the company tried to engage Warner, superintendent of the Coventry Canal, to take charge of construction, but he was not available, and the committee thereupon secured Thomas Newbold, who had engineered much of the Ashby Canal. His assistant was Francis Breedon of Saddington, a former tenant of the lands on which the reservoir there was made, whose family was to remain closely connected with both Union Canals for many years.

Expenditure on the new works, at first moderate, soon became very heavy, reaching a pinnacle of £6,443 1s 6d (£6,443.7½) for the first half year in 1808. The LNU was by then nearing its objective—soon after, it was advertising for 100–150 labourers for the Great Bowden–Harborough section.[69] But the cost of the line had already far exceeded the estimate: ultimately it amounted to about £43,000. The sequel was inevitable. The General Committee, on consulting the GJ and Trent & Mersey companies, found that these bodies would not join in if a subscription were set on foot to raise money to take the LNU line on to the GJ, though both companies thought that many of their proprietors would. In view of this, and noting that only 4 per cent of the LNU's capital remained uncalled, it recommended to the General Assembly on 16 May 1808 that the line should finish permanently at Market Harborough. The meeting adjourned to 30 May to give proprietors time to think it over, and on that day the thirty-seven shareholders present voted in favour of ending their canal at Harborough.[70] The wheel had come full circle.

The line was ready for its formal opening on 13 October 1809, and the company made much of it.[71] At 12.30pm, the General Committee members, with a body of proprietors and a band, proceeded in 'a barge and two boats' dressed with flags, from Gallow Hill wharf to Harborough, between banks lined with enthusiastic spectators. At Great Bowden wharf, they were joined by eight barges laden with coal and other goods, and the whole flotilla passed in state to Harborough 'bason' to the cheers of thousands of onlookers. Then followed a procession, the committee being preceded by 'engineers, navigators, and bargemen, carrying instruments, tools, and implements descriptive of their several occupations—two barge horses, streamers, flags . . .' to the Angel Inn, where they partook of 'an elegant and sumptuous dinner'. Many toasts were drunk, so that 'the evening concluded with hilarity and general conviviality'. Even the navvies, though 'plentifully regaled with ale', behaved themselves, and the townsfolk made a public holiday of the occasion, with 'foot races and ass races' at intervals throughout the afternoon.

The committee must have been painfully aware that any sumptuousness in the dinner was due to the generosity of Joseph Cradock of Gumley, long a friend and benefactor of the LNU. On this occasion, he had sent gifts of venison and fish, the company's celebration dinner being otherwise nothing more than the Angel's 'ordinary', or table d'hôte, for which the guests paid 3s 6d (17½p). But at least the committee had the relief of knowing that they could hand over the task of driving the waterway through the Northamptonshire uplands to others, and, indeed, had already done so (see Chapter 2); and that in the end, the Leicestershire & Northamptonshire Union Canal had turned out to be but the Harborough Navigation writ large.

CHAPTER 2

The Grand Union Canal, 1808-14

If the LNU proprietors were dismayed by the final abandonment of their ambitions to link their canal with the GJ, the supporters of the latter must have been no less so; for it seemed to put the prospect of trade from the East Midlands coming on to their line for ever beyond the hope of fulfilment. The GJ had already indicated, in response to LNU queries, that it would not support financially, as a company, LNU extension plans, but that many of its proprietors might be expected to do so. This was a line which it continued to take, and events showed that it was right in doing so—the money was ultimately raised largely in the way anticipated, and the GJ was subsequently spared a line which was little more than a liability for many years.

THE FOUNDATIONS (1808–10)

When it decided to abandon its planned line south of Harborough, the LNU resolved to make all relevant papers in its possession available to anybody willing to undertake the extension.[1] As if this hint were not broad enough, it sent a committee member, Richard Gresley, prominent also in the GJ company, to report this decision to the General Assembly of the latter on 7 June 1808.[2] The reaction was so swift that it is most probable that negotiations had been in progress since the news of the likelihood of the LNU's giving up had become publicly known as a result of their meeting on 16 May: a meeting was announced to discuss the question on 11 June 1808. This gathering had the strongest possible flavour of the GJ about it, though that body had no official connection with the new project: the chairman was William Praed (also chairman of the GJ), the legal business was from the first handled by Sale, the GJ clerk, and it was held at the Crown and Anchor Tavern in the Strand, London, a favourite venue of GJ meetings. After the reports of Barnes and Telford had been read and considered, the meeting agreed to go ahead with a scheme for making the canal to link the LNU and the GJ, a joint survey being commissioned from Telford and Benjamin Bevan, of Leighton Buzzard, an engineer who was engaged on the GJ and who was apparently highly regarded by that company. As the LNU had been through all this before, and had agreed to Telford's plan, it is possible that the new promoters were cautiously leaving themselves the option of discarding the latter's scheme. The capital to be sought was £220,000 'or other necessary sum', in £100 shares and £50 half shares, the maximum holding to be £1,000 in either. Two clerks were appointed for the time being, Richard Cowlishaw Sale of the GJ and John Edward Carter, clerk of the LNU. The canal was to be called the 'Grand Union', a logical title since it was to join the GJ and the LNU; but seemingly a revival of an earlier name, as it appears, applied to the LNU, in a Leicester paper of 1792.[3] A committee of sixteen was elected; the members were almost exclusively representative of the London interest, and this remained true of the GU for many years.

A number of shares were reserved for landowners on the line, and Gresley was asked to attend a meeting at Market Harborough (at which Telford and Bevan were also invited to be present) on 5 July 1808 to receive their subscriptions. He was also to get the documents relating to the extension from the LNU. As so often, things did not quite happen in the way directed by the resolutions. Telford's connection with the new scheme was severed virtually before it was made. The Clerk was directed to write to him on 13 June 1808, asking him to attend a committee meeting to give his opinion on the line, Bevan also to be present. There is no record that he ever did so, and henceforth Bevan's name alone occurs as engineer to the new venture. Typical, too, was the postponement of the Harborough meeting to 11 July. There was to be a large cattle fair in Leicester on 5 July, and the LNU, which knew its Leicestershire country gentry better than the City men of the GU did, thought that this would be a greater attraction to the landowners than a canal meeting, and advised postponement.

At this meeting, Bevan was unable to present a recommended line as directed. The withdrawal of Telford had relieved him from the embarrassment of working with a colleague who was among the most eminent men in the profession, and of whose plan it is evident that he disapproved. But he was now exposed to the ideas of the enthusiastic amateur—in this case, a member of the committee, Walter William Fell, who had been told that a line from the LNU near Blaby to the Oxford Canal near Cosford, just north of Rugby, would be cheaper and shorter than the intended one. Barnes was consulted, and as a result of his reply, the committee told Bevan to survey this line; if he found it unsuitable, he was to go over Telford's line again, and try to deviate it between Maidwell and Holdenby, where the local landowner, Sir William Langham of Cottesbrooke Hall, objected 'decidedly' to having the canal through one of his plantations. It was realised that the LNU would object to a scheme which involved the use of its canal by through traffic for only a few miles before it branched off at Blaby, instead of travelling the whole length of the LNU to Harborough and so paying the greatest possible toll as in Telford's scheme, and a vague promise was made to the LNU that its interests would not be forgotten. But Bevan evidently reported unfavourably on 9 July 1808, and the project was given up. Nevertheless, Bevan must have seen the advantages which a line in this direction would have, compared with any line possible through the difficult country south of Harborough, and the idea of a canal to the Oxford instead of the GJ remained in his mind, to emerge in a later stage in the GU's search for a practicable route. For the moment, he came out strongly against Telford's line at a committee meeting on 25 July. It was, he said, not possible to vary it to avoid Langham's plantation; and the line would cost £350,000. This latter point do doubt carried more weight with the committee than any landowner's objection, and to make his obvious desire for the line's abandonment still more persuasive, Bevan went on to say that Barnes's route, with a few minor variations, could be made for under £200,000. Naturally, the committee accepted this, and agreed to recommend Barnes's line as amended by Bevan to the next General Assembly. It also strengthened itself by co-opting new members, making the full committee twenty-nine strong. The General Assembly was held on the same day. It agreed to adopt Barnes-revised-Bevan as the line, an additional feature in the latter's favour being that it was 7 miles shorter than Telford's. Another important decision was made at the same meeting. Whether the canal was to be broad or narrow had been discussed earlier, the committee having been told on 9 July 1808 by Harvey, the GJ superintendent, that the GJ would not permit wide boats to pass through Blisworth tunnel (not unreasonably, since this would necessitate one-way traffic working and cause delays). At the same time, it was reported that traders likely to use the GU said that they would employ narrow boats even if the canal were made wide. The committee therefore recommended that the canal should be a narrow one, and this was accepted by the General Assembly, which thereby eased its own financial burden at the expense of future generations.

Perhaps it is unfair to blame the committee, who knew that the financial prospects were not rosy; only £117,110 had been subscribed. Whether because Gresley, the LNU's representative, had exceeded his instructions in promising financial support from that company's subscribers, or because they had read too much into his statements, the committee wrote to the LNU deploring the fact that far less had been subscribed to the scheme by LNU proprietors than the GU had been led to expect.

The LNU was asked to put pressure on its reluctant shareholders to subscribe—unless this were done, there was little hope of filling the subscription. The LNU, thus arraigned, indignantly denied having made any promises.

The committee also wrote to 'some of the principal proprietors' of the GJ and of the canals to the north of its intended line. One of these appeals which has survived was sent to Sir Justinian Isham, in his capacity as a considerable shareholder in the LNU, having been written by Carter in his role of clerk to both GU and LNU.[4] He bases his appeal on the rise of LNU shares to £40 since the GU has been mooted, and their probable fall to £20 if the scheme fails; and the likelihood that, if this happens, the GJ will find some other way to get access to the Trent, 'and then the loss to the Union Compa. will be incalculable'. But there was little response to the appeal: on 27 August, the committee was told that only £127,750 had been subscribed, so they postponed the General Assembly fixed for September until further notice, and in the meantime, subscribers were to be told that they could increase their holdings above ten shares, or twenty half shares.

In an effort to stimulate support, a public meeting was held in Coventry on 30 August 1808, Richard Gresley being in the chair. The meeting, hearing an optimistic forecast that the GU would pay a 10 per cent dividend, voted in favour of the project, but it added that John Woodhouse, acting engineer on the Northern District of the GJ, should be associated with Bevan in planning the route. It seems that there was no disagreement about the line from the LNU to Crick, but that there were two possible lines beyond that place, and the meeting wanted full information about them. They also wanted Woodhouse to be associated with Bevan in the construction of the GU; evidently there was quite a Woodhouse lobby.[5] The committee, however, was not impressed, and said that it preferred Bevan's line to that of Woodhouse, as the former's was cheaper. It refused to commission a survey from Woodhouse, or to appoint an official engineer until the Act was passed, and reiterated that

LNU support fell far below what had been promised; probably it was sore with Gresley.

That the committee was in earnest is shown by the appearance soon after this of the notices of the company's intention of applying to Parliament for powers to make the canal: on 9 September 1808, the *Leicester Journal* carried an announcement that the company would apply for an Act authorising the making of a canal from the LNU at Foxton to the GJ at Willoughby, near to the GJ's termination. In the issue of 16 September, however, this notice is repeated, but another appears beneath it. In this second notice, the GU repeats its determination to apply for an Act, but the line given is from the LNU at Foxton to the GJ at Norton, near Long Buckby, the line being the same as the earlier one as far as Crick, but then striking south by way of Watford to the GJ.[6]

The options were thus left open, but the decision about the line was soon taken, plans being deposited with the Clerks of the Peace for Leicestershire and Northamptonshire respectively on 28 and 29 September.[7] The line from Crick to Willoughby had been selected. But Bevan had evidently been thinking over the possibility of linking with the Oxford rather than directly with the GJ. Reporting to the committee on 31 October 1808, he pointed out that his line would cost £180,000, and only £136,000 had been subscribed. He added, however, that he had 'nearly ascertained' that a line from the LNU to Hillmorton on the Oxford was practicable, and that it would cost a mere £110,000. With its finances in such a dubious state, it is not surprising that the committee thereupon decided to call off the intended application to Parliament while Bevan did a thorough survey of his Hillmorton line. To leave no avenue unexplored, it ordered him also to look at the line proposed by Woodhouse to the GJ. Probably it was impressed by the fact that the latter was 5 miles shorter than Bevan's—though, as the latter pointed out, it included a tunnel ¾ miles long, and would take a year longer to make.

Bevan's report went into considerable detail about his Fox-

Page 53 (*above*) Debdale wharf. The southern terminal of the LNU from 1797 to 1809; (*below*) swing bridge, Foxton. Bought from the GU for £20 and brought here from Watford in 1886, to replace an earlier 'swivel bridge'. The LNU kept it locked and paid the keeper £2.70 a year

Page 54 (*above*) Great Bowden cutting. A picturesque feature of the 1809 extension; the LNU planted 1,100 trees here in 1888, at a cost of £3.50; (*below*) Market Harborough canal basin

ton–Willoughby plan. It was for a canal 31¼ miles long, no less than 31 miles being on one level, climbing the 74ft from the LNU to its summit by twelve locks, and locking down 52ft at Willoughby into the GJ by nine locks (the shallowness of the locks being to conserve water). The cost of the line itself would be £142,219, to which must be added £37,781 for reservoirs, law and other expenses, a total of £180,000. He ends by pointing out that, while his line would take three years to construct, and Woodhouse's four, a line from North Kilworth to Hillmorton would take only two years, in addition to which it would shorten the distance to 24 miles from the LNU and reduce the cost to £140,000. He winds up that if the Hillmorton line on closer inspection looks as good as it does now, 'I think there will be but one Opinion upon the subject of which line should be preferred'.

He still thought so after a closer inspection of the line, and the committee wrote to the Oxford Canal Company asking for an abatement of tolls on goods passing into and out of their canal along the GU, should this line be made. Taking no chances on a favourable reply, it heard Bevan's findings on the various possibilities for a tunnel near Crick, one being unavoidable if they took the more southerly course recommended by Woodhouse. It was well that it did so, for, after reading the Oxford's answer, and various other letters relating to it, the committee abandoned the Hillmorton idea, and even gave up Bevan's original plan of a line to Braunston or Willoughby.

Instead, it ordered Bevan and Woodhouse to make separate surveys and plans of the three routes available by tunnels near Crick. Bevan and Woodhouse accordingly delivered their plans for the committee's inspection on 29 May 1809, and the committee chose a line passing through the hill west of Crick village by a 43 chain tunnel, the line being shortened by carrying it over valleys near Crick on two embankments. Bevan estimated the cost at £54,703, Woodhouse at £44,732 (these figures were, of course, for the Crick–GJ section only), to which had to be added the cost of the embankments, thought likely to be about £3,000. The subscription list had flagged, being still only £137,000, and Gresley, Harvey, and Fell were commissioned to write a prospectus to revive it, which they did to such good effect that by June the figure had risen to £165,000. The General Assembly on 7 June 1809, having been presented with the committee's views, adopted the line from Foxton by way of Crick to Long Buckby, a distance of some 24 miles, the cost of which Bevan estimated at not more than £205,000. Nine more names were added to the committee, and William Tyringham Praed, son of William Praed, treasurer and a committeeman of the Grand Junction, was appointed treasurer.

Subscriptions, hitherto hard to get, now came pouring in, and by 9 June no less than £211,450 had been promised. As deposits had not been paid on fifty shares, the committee accepted a further £14,900 of provisional subscriptions before closing the list. A subcommittee of seven members had already been set up to frame the clauses of the Bill, and the committee began to think of tonnages and their relations with their neighbours, especially the LNU. Under the latter's original scheme, the distance from Leicester to the GJ via Northampton was 49 miles, giving a total tonnage of 11s 8¾d (59p). The GU felt that tonnages on the new route should not exceed this, although the line via Long Buckby to Gayton was 5 miles longer. It therefore proposed that it should deduct 3d from the tonnage on merchandise along the GU, while the LNU deducted 2d. On coal, it proposed to take 2s 11d (14½p), while the LNU would receive 2s 1d (10½p). It also deliberated tonnages on goods not passing through the GU locks, and even details such as 'ffrauds by Boatmen' received the committee's attention. The principle by which the GU would abide, it said, was that the public should not be placed in a worse position than it would have occupied if the original line via Northampton had been made. After its years of penury, the LNU was less inclined to be high minded, but Fell attended its General Assembly on 20 November and got the principle of equalisation of tonnages between the parliamentary and proposed lines, 'tho' somewhat objected to at first', recognised. But the LNU would make no concessions to the GU over coal tonnages, fearing that this would lead to the removal to the GU of the centre of coal distribution, at that time Harborough.

Having removed this obstacle, the GU set to work to dispose of a more serious one, the opposition of the Nene Commissioners, supported by the townsfolk of Northampton, who demanded that the promised canal link from their town to the GJ must be made within a specified time, to replace the tramroad with which they had been fobbed off by the GJ, and that tonnages between Leicester and Northampton must not exceed those imposed by the 1793 Act. It was generally acknowledged that this opposition would be sufficient to defeat the Bill, and a meeting of delegates of the GU (Mills and Fell), LNU (Paget, Wood, and Sprigg), and GJ (Praed, Inglis, and Harvey—all three committee members of the GU as well) was held at Woburn on 3 January 1810 to placate the commissioners. The delegates agreed that the GJ should make a cut to Northampton at its own expense, and the GU and LNU should guarantee 5 per cent on the cost of making both the branch canal and the existing railway. The gesture was completely successful, the commissioners withdrawing their objections.[8] The GU and LNU took the opportunity also of coming to an agreement about tolls: coal from the LNU passing along the GU beyond Bosworth tunnel but not more than 18 miles along the line was to pay 5s (25p) per ton in equal portions to the two companies. For coal passing farther than 18 miles, the GU was to get 2s 11d (14½p), the LNU 2s 1d (10½p) per ton. The locks at the north end of the GU were to be precisely the same lift and dimensions as those at the south, to give the LNU the same advantages of water as the GJ. Coal from the GJ along the GU was to pay 2s 6d (12½p) per ton up to 12 miles, then 2½d per ton additional, to a maximum of 5s (25p) per ton. On coal passing from the GU along the LNU, the GU was to give up half its tonnage. So pleased was the committee with the result of these complicated negotiations, that it decided to try for toll reductions by agreement on these lines rather than by putting clauses in the Bill, and negotiations began for the purchase of land for Sulby reservoir while the Bill was still before Parliament. Its euphoria was shared; GJ shares rose to £234[9].But there still remained hurdles to be cleared. The town of Aylesbury, indignant at the GJ's failure to make a promised branch canal to serve the town, staged a public meeting, at which it was resolved that, since the making of the GU might further delay, if not entirely prevent, that of the Marsworth–Aylesbury cut, the town would oppose the GU Bill, and would seek the support of the local MPs.[10] The threat was taken seriously by the GJ, which called a Special Assembly on 29 March 1810 to discuss ways of circumventing the obstacle. The method quite obviously was to buy off the Aylesburians as Northampton had already been won over; and that this was done appears from a note in the *Northampton Mercury* a month later to the effect that no opposition was expected from Aylesbury 'in consequence of the intended canal from Marsworth to Abingdon'.[11] The GU itself played no part in these negotiations, although they were largely the work of its own committee members wearing their GJ hats, but continued its elevated course of seeing that nobody suffered because its new line was to replace the Northampton one. It offered compensation to any canal company which might be harmed by the change, and, perhaps in anticipation of a spate of claims, made a £1 per share call on its proprietors. One early claimant was the Oxford, which wanted compensating for the loss of coal trade likely to be caused by the opening of the GU—presumably to south Leicestershire and north Northamptonshire. In one of those complicated toll agreements with which it was involved throughout its independent life, the GU, while believing that any loss the Oxford suffered would be more than made up by the trade between that canal and the Nene, offered it the same compensation on coal from the LNU to points between Crick and Gayton, or to the Oxford, as the Oxford would give the

GU on coal from the Oxford to Northampton. This did not satisfy the Oxford, which demanded guaranteeing against Derbyshire coal going into the Oxford from the GU without paying 2s 9d (14p) per ton as Staffordshire coal did. The committee said it would do this if possible.

Such opposition as remained was largely concentrated among owners of lands on the Avon, who feared that the GU would tamper with their water supply. Clauses to safeguard them were put in the Bill, and the committee asked Bevan to report on the position as regards the supply of water to the line. He replied by quoting a survey he had carried out three years earlier for the GJ, which was at that time contemplating making a reservoir in the Watford area, in the vicinity of which the GU was to run. Revising his conclusions (that every square mile of the district produced 995 GJ locksful of water in an average year) to fit the smaller GU locks of 3,860cu ft capacity, he calculated that 61,883 locksful would be collected annually from this district, and of this total, the GU could take 36,333 before the river supplies were touched: this, amounting to nearly 100 locks a day, would permit 'a very ample trade', as he justly remarks.

The Bill had a quiet passage through Parliament. The estimate presented for the line was £219,000, of which £69,000 was for the 93 chains of tunnelling with the associated deep cutting. The 21 locks were to cost £16,800, and the 46 bridges £8,300. The £16,229 allowed for reservoirs and collecting drains also included 'Steam Engines', presumably for pumping water from nearby streams into the canal (at least one steam engine was used in the construction of the canal, but there is no evidence that the canal actually employed them in its operation). It was estimated that 5 miles of the line would need puddling, and £7,000 was allowed for this; an expensive item, for digging the level parts was estimated as only £10,350. Most of the subscribers were down for fairly small holdings, of five or fewer shares. The two largest, George Moubray and Robert Sutton, subscribed for thirty shares each, while Reginald Grahame and

George Scott were entered for twenty-five each. Among the nine subscribers for twenty shares is William Praed, while William Tyringham Praed had ten. There was one subscriber with fifteen shares, and a few with ten. Rather more than half the landowners on the line had signified their assent to the scheme (including the once obstructive Sir John Palmer), but there was no active opposition, and at least one, a widow, escaped committing herself—she 'would not be seen'.[12] The Bill therefore came eventually before the House of Lords Committee on Unopposed Private Bills, under the chairmanship of Lord Spencer, a great Northamptonshire landowner. Apart from the fact that a representative had to appear to give consent to the scheme on behalf of one of the landowners who had got himself made a prisoner-of-war in France, there was no feature of interest in that body's inspection of the project, and it ordered the Bill to be reported without amendment.[13] On 24 May 1810, the Royal Assent was given.

THE ACT (1810)

The company's Act (50 Geo III, c 122), after reciting the two Acts of the LNU, stated that a new canal from the LNU in Gumley parish to the GJ in Norton parish would 'open a short and easy Communication between the populous and manufacturing Towns in the Counties of *Leicester* and *Warwick*' and authorised the making of such a canal by 338 named individuals, who were incorporated as 'The Company of Proprietors of the Grand Union Canal'. It is significant of the changed climate of canal promotion as well as of the London-orientated character of the Grand Union that not a single peer is listed, and of the four baronets, only one, Sir Justinian Isham, was primarily a country gentleman (though a baronet, Sir James Duberly, became the largest shareholder, having collected no fewer than 172 shares by 1814).

The new canal was to leave the LNU near Foxton, and was to run by way of Lubenham, Theddingworth, Husbands Bos-

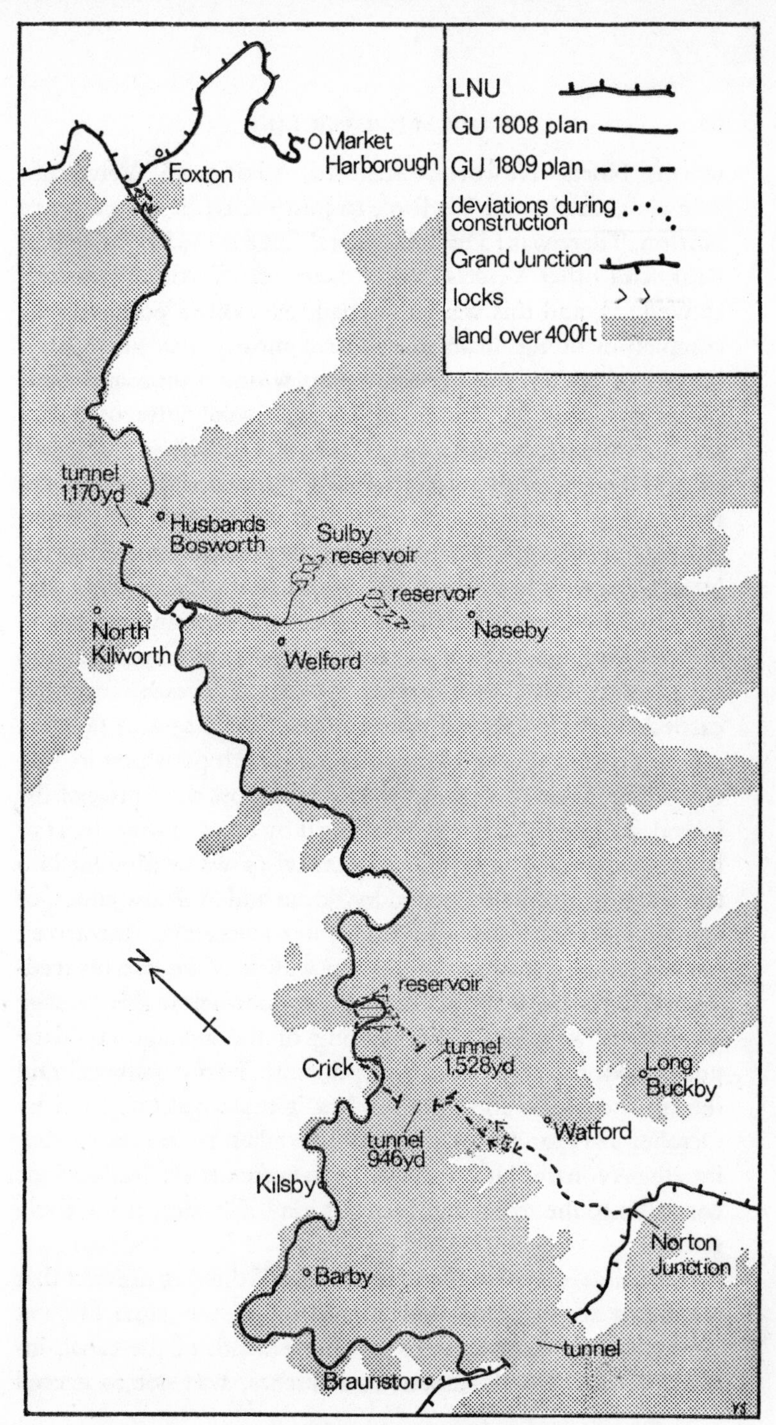

FIGURE 2. Map of GU, 1808 and 1809 schemes and deviations (Scale: 1in = 2¾ m)

worth, North Kilworth, Stanford, Elkington, Yelvertoft, Winwick, Crick, and Watford, to join the GJ in the parish of Norton. There was to be a 'Collateral Cut for the Navigation of Boats and other Vessels' to the Leicester–Northampton road at Welford, and this was to be made as soon as possible after completion of the main line. The company was given wide powers of taking water from streams within a thousand yards of the canal or its branch, and could make 'Fire or Steam Engines' for use in respect of this. It was forbidden, however, to tap streams which had hitherto flowed into the GJ, the LNU, or the Oxford without the consent of these companies, although nothing in this clause was to prevent its making the intended reservoir at Crick. The Avon was to be passed under the canal by a tunnel, and the waters of its main course and feeders were not to be touched before they reached Stanford Park, apart from any surplus above the average quantity carried by the combined watercourses of the system (a small stream flowing through Husbands Bosworth parish on its way to join the Avon was excluded, as it lay across the course of the intended tunnel and might be affected by the working shafts to be sunk there). The 'average quantity' of water flowing into the Avon was to be measured by Bevan and William James, of Warwick, during the months from July to December (inclusive), 1811. The GU was not to reduce the waters in the streams feeding the Avon so as to diminish the amount below this average quantity at any time. The gauging of the average could be postponed if there were exceptionally heavy falls of rain during the observation period, but it must be completed by October 1813, and no water could be taken from that passing into the Avon until it was done. There were detailed regulations controlling the company's extraction of water from these streams.

Regarding the dimensions of the canal, the Act ordered that the locks at the north end should be of the same lift and dimensions as those at the south. The width of the canal, including towing-path, fences, and ditches, was not to exceed

20yd, except at basins, etc, and where it was on an embankment or in a cutting.

Small pieces of land cut off by the canal from the main part of an estate were to be bought by the company, except that in Stanford, such small pieces, belonging to Henry Otway of Stanford Hall, were to be laid to other lands of his at the GU's expense. Otherwise, the company could resell the lands it did not want.

A capital of not more than £250,000 was authorised, in £100 shares and £50 half shares; if this were found to be insufficient, a further £50,000 could be raised by the proprietors among themselves, by the admission of new subscribers, by mortgage, or by promissory notes. Landowners claiming the privilege within twelve months of the passing of the Act could subscribe for one share for each one-eighth of a mile of their land through which the canal passed, providing they did not already hold twenty or more shares. Each share carried with it a vote at the company's Assemblies, but no proprietor was to have more than ten votes, or to act as proxy for more than ten other proprietors. The first of these Assemblies was to be held at the Crown and Anchor Tavern at 11am on 4 June 1810, the second on 5 November, and subsequent ones on the first Monday in each June and November, each Assembly to appoint the meeting place for the next. The June Assembly was to elect a General Committee of twenty-one members (having a quorum of seven), each of whom must hold at least five shares and not be in possession of any office in the company. The committee had the general supervision of the canal, the appointment and dismissal of staff (except the Clerk and Treasurer, who were to be elected and dismissed by the General Assembly) and the promulgation of bye-laws for the company. However, no committee could be elected by a General Assembly at which there were not present, in person or by proxy, holders of at least 700 shares. Should the shares represented fall below this number, a fresh Assembly must be summoned for the following week, and every proprietor not present in person or represented by proxy should be fined 10s (50p). The General Committee was to appoint two subcommittees annually, each consisting of seven or more proprietors, with a quorum of three, each holding at least five shares, to carry out such duties as the General Committee delegated to them. Calls on the shares were to be made by the General Committee, each call not exceeding £10 and being not less than three months distant from its predecessor.

To reimburse themselves for the 'great Charges and Expence' they would incur in making the canal, the proprietors were allowed to charge the following tolls:

Coal or coke from the GJ passing not more than 12 miles on the GU—2s 6d (12½p) per ton. Beyond 12 miles but not passing on to the LNU—2½d per ton per mile.
Coal or coke from the LNU passing not more than 18 miles on the GU—2s 6d (12½p) per ton. Beyond 18 miles, a further 2½d per ton per mile to a maximum of 2s 11d (14½p) per ton.
Coal or coke from the LNU to the Oxford Canal—an additional 2s 9d (14p) over the above 2s 11d (14½p).
Lime, dung, manure, and limestone, passing a lock—1s 3d (6p) per ton.
Cattle, sheep, swine, and other beasts, stone, bricks, tiles, slates, sand, ironstone, pig iron, pig lead, passing a lock—2s 6d (12½p) per ton.
All other goods passing a lock—3s (15p) per ton.

Several clauses tied the GU's hands in dealing with the all-important coal traffic. It was not allowed to lower the tonnage below 2s 6d (12½p) per ton on coal entering from the LNU without the latter's consent, or to lower the additional 2s 9d (14p) per ton on that passing to the Oxford unless that company agreed—this was especially complicated, for the Oxford was at the same time bound to reduce in like proportion the tonnage on coal entering its line from the Coventry and the Warwick & Napton canals. If rates were reduced on coal from the GJ on to the GU, there was to be a similar reduction on coal from the LNU passing more than 7 miles on the GU. The LNU agreed to reduce tolls on coal passing its whole length—for which the full tonnage was 3s 9d (19p)—and proceeding beyond Husbands Bosworth tunnel to no farther than 18 miles on the GU, to 2s 6d (12½p) per ton; farther than 18 miles, to 2s 1d (10½p). Coal passing from the GU to the LNU was to pay 2s 6d (12½p) per ton. The purpose of this complex tariff system, hedged round by safeguards for all parties strong enough to influence the GU Bill's chances in Parliament, and clearly the result of much hard bargaining behind the scenes, was to safeguard the interests of the Staffordshire and Warwickshire coalfields on the one hand, and the Leicester and Derbyshire on the other, in the areas where they already had the lion's share of the trade; as well as to see that none of the existing canals lost trade they already enjoyed.

There follow the usual operational regulations. Sadly prophetic of future troubles is the clause permitting boats with less loading than 20 tons to pass the locks on payment for the actual weight carried, when there was insufficient water to pass the full 20 tons. Other clauses protected the supply of water: boatmen could be fined for using shafts tipped with iron points less than 10sq in in area at the tip (to protect the puddled bottom), and there is a lengthy description of how boats should be worked through locks, and the manner of procedure when boats were approaching a lock from above and below simultaneously. Whether the average boater would have been able to understand the stilted lawer's English of the Act, if he could have read it, is doubtful, but the five pound fine for infringement was no doubt more effective. (Incidentally, the GU called 'paddles' what the LNU called 'cloughs', perhaps a reflection of the latter's connection with the north, the former's with the GJ).

As usual, landowners' rights were safeguarded and their interests looked after. Landowners along the canal were to be allowed to carry manure and lime for fertilising their fields toll free (providing that they made good any damage done to the banks by their boats), unless the boats passed any lock, when toll became payable. Fishery rights were reserved to them, either as lords of the manors through which the canal passed, or as landowners therein. They were permitted to make wharfs on their own lands adjoining the canal (though if they did not, and the committee thought that they should have done, the company was empowered to make the wharfs after giving three months' notice). Wharfages at such private wharfs were to be restricted, and the wharfs were not to be used by one person exclusively. One landowner was singled out for special mention: Henry Otway, of Stanford Hall. The company was not to make any wharf (or its appurtenances), reservoir, or even winding hole for turning boats, in his estates—though as the canal here passed through a lonely region consisting of the deserted lands of three villages depopulated in the Middle Ages, it is in any case unlikely that it would have squandered its resources in doing any of these things.

A group of clauses of some complexity deals with the GU's relations with other canals. It was to pay the Oxford 2s 9d (14p) per ton on coal and coke passing from the LNU to the Oxford, the payments being made every six months. Furthermore, if the Oxford's receipts from its traffic to Northampton were not equal to those from traffic along its line to Stretton, Clifton, Brownsover, Hillmorton, and Braunston wharfs (ie those likely to be affected by the coming of the GU), together with receipts which the Oxford would have had if coal from the GU on to the GJ, travelling no farther than Weedon, had come from the Oxford instead, then the GU was to make up the difference. To ensure that there should be no deception, each company was ordered to supply copies of the relevant traffic returns to the other. The Coventry, Warwick & Napton, and Warwick & Birmingham companies were to be awarded 'such and the like Compensation, to be ascertained in the like Time and Manner, on the like Conditions', which left their clerks with the unenviable tasks of sorting out the long and almost incomprehensible clause relating to the Oxford, and applying it to their own concerns as best they could. The Trent & Mersey was to be compensated also, on the grounds that the new canal would injure it more than the previously authorised line of the LNU, through Northampton, would have done. The Act, having made this questionable assertion, made no attempt to lay down any means of ascertaining how much, if any, harm the T & M would suffer, but washes its hands of the whole matter by referring the verdict to a jury in the event of a dispute over it between the companies—a most probable event, one would think. The Birmingham Canal Navigations got a similar clause.

Saddled by such obligations, the new company started under a burden which the years were not to lighten. But two clauses point to the future, and show the promoters looking forward optimistically to further developments. In the first, the GU company is empowered to make its canal suitable for barges (ie wide boats), should the GJ relent and allow them through Blisworth tunnel. The second, doubtless connected with this, permits the company, if it so wishes, to replace the locks at both ends of its line with inclined planes. There is no indication that at the time of the Act, the GU had any intention of doing so, but ninety years later, when the old company had gone out of existence, this clause was to take spectacular effect.

CONSTRUCTION (1810–14)

The first General Assembly of the company, held on 4 June 1810, restricted the capital to 2,450 shares; surplus shares were to be bought in. To meet immediate requirements, a call was made which, with the two calls made before the passing of the Act, brought the total called-up capital to 10 per cent. The required General Committee of twenty-one members was elected, William Praed being in the chair. Sale and Carter were elected clerks, Sale being the senior and ranking as principal clerk to the company. It may be noted here that, in contrast to the LNU, very little work, be it organisational, administrative, or financial, was entrusted by the GU to local men; perhaps wisely, for its relations with Carter do not seem to have been too happy—the committee severely censured him on one occasion for neglecting to summon the company's largest shareholder to meetings of the committee, of which he was naturally a member. The first General Committee meeting, on 13 and 14 June, settled a number of lesser matters (as, for instance, the design of the seal, which bore the devices of the LNU and GJ side by side, surmounted by a classically draped figure reclining alongside a watercourse), but its most important action was the appointment of Bevan as engineer—a lucrative post, carrying with it the salary of £500 per annum and £200 travelling expenses; thereby setting an example of generous pay which extended to other officers and was to be severely criticised in the lean years ahead. The two subcommittees—a Subcommittee in the Country, to supervise construction, and a London Subcommittee, to look after finance, were appointed, of thirteen and fourteen members respectively. After the frustrations of previous years, the committee was in a hurry to get matters moving, and ordered the two land valuers it appointed to offer 'liberal terms' for a quick sale, and a 10 per cent bonus to owners of not more than one furlong crossed by the canal if they accepted the company's offer without delay. The GU also decided that it wanted its own London premises, and an eighteen-roomed house, 10 Norfolk Street, was taken on lease. It recouped itself to some extent by letting Sale live in it rent free, in return for which he made no charge for his services as the company's clerk.

It was already in trouble. The money so freely promised by subscribers was less readily forthcoming in reality than in prospect, and the £10 per cent call was readvertised, non-payers being threatened with forfeiture. (The arrears were £1,146, and most of the holders of these shares had sold out). In order to reduce costs by avoiding a short tunnel at Watford, Bevan was considering asking the consent of the local great lady, Mrs. Bennett, to a deviation of his line which would take it through her park. A deviation was also to be made at Foxton, to avoid an embankment, but this was within the limits of permitted deviation. Bevan had now decided that he wanted to build Foxton locks as a staircase, with side ponds, on the grounds that time, water, and money would be saved, though more land would have to be bought for the side ponds, and this was accepted by the committee.[14] Some of those in the inner councils of the GU availed themselves of the knowledge they gained to sell out while the going was good: Pares and Heygate, the Leicester bankers, both unloaded their shares and left the subcommittee. But the less well-informed still had confidence, and LNU shares, once down to £16, rose to £135.[15]

Work was now in progress at the northern end of the line. A good deal of the land had been bought (including nearly 38 acres, for £3,100, for Sulby reservoir). A contract had also been made with two brickmakers to deliver 2 million bricks at Crick at 32s (£1.60) per thousand. Over 350 men were at work by 23 March 1811. Their rate of pay was 4¼d per cu yd of earth dug and wheeled one stage, the workmen finding all materials and levelling the earth every 4ft in embankments. For every further stage the earth was wheeled, 1d extra was added, to a maximum payment of 9¾d for six stages (the extra ½d came from a ¼d bonus added for the fourth and fifth stages). As so often, it was difficult to keep the men on the site, and a bonus scheme was instituted in an attempt to dissuade them from wandering off in search of work in the Fens.

Bricks were also being made at Foxton, and Bevan hit upon the idea of laying a tramroad or light railway alongside the line of the locks to facilitate the transport of bricks to them. It could also be used when the canal was completed as far as Husbands Bosworth tunnel to lessen the expense of the carriage of materials thither.[16] The subcommittee told him to get second-hand rails, but subsequently altered its mind, in view of the greater value of new plates when the company had finished with them and wanted to sell them.[17] Railway plates were therefore ordered from the Butterley Company; there was some delay in their delivery, but they were being laid in January 1811.

Trouble was now experienced with land for the reservoirs,

Bevan reporting that trial borings on the site of that at Naseby showed that a fifth of the area would require puddling—a much larger proportion than had been estimated—at an additional expense of £2,000. The subcommittee ordered him to look for another site, which must have caused him some anxiety, for it was already believed that the land above the site planned for Naseby reservoir was unsuitably porous. But luck and perseverance came to Bevan's aid. He found by further borings higher up the valley above the proposed Naseby site, that the porosity was only superficial, and that a 59-acre reservoir was possible there; moreover, 51 acres of this area were available for purchase. The committee approved the site, and added that if Bevan were decidedly (a favourite word of the committee) of opinion that the GU should have the Sulby site as well, he should go ahead with the scheme for a reservoir there, too.

At this point, on 2 October 1811, the committee sent a deputation of its members to see how things were shaping. It found that four of the five miles between Foxton and Bosworth tunnel had been cut. All eight of the working shafts at the tunnel had been sunk, headings had been driven through, water was being cleared out of the pits, and 12ft of brickwork had been done. At the point where the canal was crossed by the turnpike road from Harborough to Lutterworth, a wharfinger's house and two rows of huts, each capable of holding 100 workmen, had been built. The line thence to the Avon and half the collateral cut had been finished and filled with water, so that workmen could boat materials to the Avon embankment. South of this embankment to Stanford, the canal was finished and filled with water. Then it rained, so the delegates contented themselves with riding over the ground chosen for Naseby and Sulby reservoirs, and then went home, taking the southern part of the line as read.

Any feelings of self-satisfaction the delegates may have experienced received a rude shock at the end of November, when Bevan reported to the subcommittee that further borings on the line of Crick tunnel, where work on the deep cutting at the

Page 71 Bridge styles on the Leicester line: (*above*) Towers' Bridge (105), Aylestone, 1794; (*below*) bridge near Gallow Hill, c 1808

Page 72 Bridge styles on the Leicester line: (*above*) Bridge 66, near Debdale, 1898; (*below*) bridge, Watford bottom lock, 1902

north end had begun, had revealed faulty strata. This was a major crisis, beyond the subcommittee's powers to solve, and it took the matter to the General Committee on 12 December 1811. This body acted with commendable swiftness, ordering Bevan to prepare comparative estimates for alternative lines and to have a committee meeting summoned within three days of his having done so.[18] This meeting was held on 1 January 1812, but it was not until 6 February that, the landowners on the alternative line suggested by Bevan having been sounded and having agreed to sell the land required for it, providing that the usual cost of an Act were divided among them, the committee decided that the authorised line should be given up in the section including the tunnel, and a new one, east of it, adopted instead.[17] They were at the same time having trouble with Bosworth tunnel, where difficulty was experienced in clearing the middle three working shafts of water. Bevan was authorised to buy a second-hand steam engine for £400 to help in the pumping. He did this, and work went ahead: 707yd of the tunnel were finished by 20 March. The engine remained on the works after the tunnel was completed, the committee ordering it to be sold on 3 November 1813. As an experiment, the committee bought a few lamps for the tunnellers' use at Bosworth, to replace their candles; but the men refused to use them, as they broke so easily. Meanwhile, the laying of the Foxton railway had been finished, and on 3 June 1812, the committee ordered that the canal should be opened for the conveyance of goods from the LNU to the north end of Bosworth tunnel.[20] By 18 September, one trader, Fox of Market Harborough, had sent 544 tons 14cwt of coal along this distance, for which he paid 4s (20p) per ton to cover tonnage and freight. How much of the journey was done by rail and how much by water is not known, but the fact that Bevan was ordered to procure 'Floats' for the trade and make arrangements for landing coal near the road at Husbands Bosworth implies that the railway section was up Foxton hill only.[21]

The committee was evidently pleased by the success of its

railway, and asked the GJ for the loan of some disused railway plates they believed were at Braunston and Wolverton, so that they could lay a track between the working shafts at Crick tunnel.[22] These were apparently not forthcoming, so Bevan was ordered to get some new plates to continue the line over the hill at Crick—perhaps the first section was formed from surplus plates from Foxton. Work was in fact going ahead very well, Bosworth tunnel being finished on 29 April 1813, and the canal opened to Stanford on the main line and Welford mill on the branch on 25 May 1813.[23]

This gratifying event gave the committee time to pause and reflect on the company's financial position, which it found to be not good. In a report to the General Assembly on 7 June 1813, it admitted that, while 11 miles of the canal were now open, it had not managed to keep within the estimate; though it drew cold comfort from the assertion that the excess was not likely to be greater than one-twelfth of the latter—'a Circumstance unparallelled in the Execution of any Undertaking of equal Magnificence'. They list the causes of the overspending. Surprisingly, the new line taken for Crick tunnel was not the chief, costing £7,000 over the estimate. Most expensive was the difficulty in draining Bosworth tunnel (£12,000 over the estimate), while land needed for the canal cost £10,000 more than had been anticipated. The decision, made when construction began, to build the bridges 22ft wide cost an extra £2,000. Another decision taken after the original estimate, 'Making the Basins at the Locks to save Water', accounted for a further £1,700. More of the bed had needed puddling than expected, and £3,500 extra was consumed thereby. No less than £6,500 was lost to wet weather and the rising cost of labour. In all, £53,100 more than forecast was likely to be spent. To meet this emergency, the Assembly approved a plan for the sale of the unsubscribed shares and the issue of new shares, which would be available to present proprietors at £75 per £100 share, up to a maximum of £50,000. Alternatively, the proprietors could subscribe for loan notes for £100 and £50 at £5 per cent per annum interest. The scheme was not, however, greeted with enthusiasm by the shareholders, only £17,525 having been subscribed by 23 July, and the clerks circularised them to prod them into taking part. The task fell to Sale alone, as Carter had recently died, and no successor in Leicester was appointed. The circular seems to have had some effect—Sir Justinian Isham, for instance, once before coaxed into subscribing, appears to have been amenable again.[24]

Construction was being pushed ahead at both ends. At Foxton, it was hoped to open the locks on 10 September 1813, but Hancock, a committee member sent to make a three-day inspection of the works, said that they would not open until 1 October. He also recommended that the line at Watford should be deviated to pass through Watford Park (an idea which had been put forward earlier), even if it cost £500 more than the parliamentary line with a tunnel built narrow with a passing place in the middle—the latter a feature strongly opposed by Bevan. The committee agreed, and negotiated with the owner, Mrs Bennett, who succeeded in imposing stiff terms—£2,000 plus £125 per acre for the land taken, the whole not to exceed four acres. She could also have a wharf, and keep a pleasure boat on the canal.[25] Later, the committee also agreed that she could nominate a suitably qualified lock keeper 'to secure civility towards herself and Tenants and also proper attention to the Boatmen to prevent their doing any Injury to her Property'. It was less accommodating about the bridge over the canal in the park, refusing an ornamental bridge on the score of cost. Later, it thought about buying a second-hand iron bridge which came up for sale. Nothing came of this, however, and eventually Mrs Bennett had to be content with a brick one, a cast-iron bridge being too expensive (about £120, the committee believed).

Work on the canal had slowed down somewhat, a spell of dry weather causing delay in the puddling at Stanford. But matters improved in the autumn. On 1 October 1813, Foxton locks opened, as Hancock had foreseen.[26] A wet spell set in, softening the ground for excavation and providing water for puddling, and work at Stanford went ahead apace. On 23 October, 789yd—a little over one-half—of Crick tunnel were finished.[27] The decision to build Watford locks 'with only three passing places' was taken.[28]

The committee was now turning its attention to minor details, among them the curious decision that bridges should be numbered, not in sequence as usual, but according to the number of the close they were in, as recorded on the official plans of the canal. The question of a horse bridge at Foxton, to allow boat horses access from one canal to the other, was discussed, the existing structure being a temporary wooden one. The LNU suggested that the need to build one could be avoided by using the first brick bridge north of Foxton; all that was necessary was for the GU to buy land to make a towpath on the opposite side of the canal to the LNU's, between Foxton bottom lock and this bridge. Bevan said that the scheme was sound, but that the LNU ought to make the new towpath. In the end, since neither was willing, they built a bridge near the bottom lock, at joint expense.

Work at Crick went on at a good pace, though there was a setback in the winter of 1814, when a fall at shaft no 10 killed a workman and held up operations. But on 29 March 1814, water was let into the canal to within a few yards of the tunnel's north entrance. By early April, work had been begun on Watford locks, and the embankments at Welton and Norton were near their full height (the committee had been seriously concerned by the slow progress of the latter; perhaps it had made this known to the contractor, Reynolds, for during a spell of frost in late January 1814, he engaged more hands and pressed ahead with earth moving). To help with the work on Norton embankment, the committee sent all available floats on a long journey by way of the Trent & Mersey to Norton. The end being in sight, it ordered that the toll clerk's house at the bottom lock at Foxton, and the lock keeper's house 'by the uppermost Lock next the Side Ponds' should be built at once.

Officers, too, were being considered, and on 1 June 1814, John Ruffell and Henry Hollyer were appointed toll clerks at Watford and Foxton respectively.

Crick tunnel was completed on 29 July 1814.[29] The main line of the canal was virtually finished, and the official opening was arranged for 9 August 1814. It was fittingly made a great occasion, the procession of boats passing over the whole of the GU from Norton Junction to Foxton, and continuing to Harborough, some 29 miles.[30] There were three boats, the first of which, fitted up 'in an elegant style' and carrying a band and flying the flags of the GU and the LNU, bore deputations from both companies and 'a large assembly of beauty and fashion'. The other two were less opulently equipped, and carried 'such ladies and gentlemen who chose to be of the party'. These were followed by two of Pickford's fly-boats, on their first commercial run to Leicester. Even in those early days, before Nature had taken over to make the canal the gem of rural beauty it is today, it must have been a charming trip. At the junction of the Welford branch, a boat from Welford met them with ample supplies of refreshments to fortify them against the passage of Bosworth tunnel. They seem to have got through the far more alarming Crick without hysteria, but at Bosworth, some of the beauty and fashion displayed 'strong symptoms of fear'. No harm was done, however: the ladies' fears were allayed by the 'gallantry and polite attention' of the lucky gentlemen, so that there was 'a close package, great hilarity, and good humour' while they were in the darkness of the tunnel, which no doubt reflects great credit on the GU's refreshments. They arrived at Harborough soon after 7pm, and after their long day in the fresh air, doubtless tucked into the 'sumptuous dinner' provided with relish. Turtle, venison, and turbot are named among the good things—provided mainly, it seems, by Joseph Cradock, who had done the same for the LNU at its opening to Harborough in 1809. Mrs Cradock presented a banner, somebody recited an ode, there was great gaiety, and 'the festive board was not departed from until a late hour'.

Pickford's fly-boats, however, dourly continued on their way to Leicester, where they arrived next day, returning thence with a cargo for London the same evening.[31]

It was indeed an occasion for rejoicing. The vision dreamed up by Dr Bree and his colleagues more than twenty years earlier had been made reality: the mines and industrial towns of the East Midlands were at last connected by a waterway with the metropolis, and the future must have looked rosy to those fortunate mortals at the sumptuous dinner. No doubt the morning after brought more sombre thoughts to the minds of the more perceptive, for the GU's position depended on too many uncertain factors for comfort.

CHAPTER 3

The Old Union Canal, 1809—63

THE YEARS OF SUCCESS (1809–47)

ITS dreams of through traffic to the London market temporarily abandoned, the LNU (whose cumbersome title was universally shortened to 'the Union', and, after the opening of the GU, 'the Old Union') set to work to develop trade on such line of country as it had. The obvious hope was Market Harborough, and trade there began to build up in a satisfying way. By December 1809, Messrs Burton & Furnival were advertising Derbyshire coal for sale at Harborough wharf, and also that they had 'boats with proper covers' to take wool and other local produce to the waterways of the north.[1] The Bowden Brewery also went in for the sale of Derbyshire coal there, in partnership with J. Dobson, while Fox, Lefevre & Mitchell likewise engaged in selling Derbyshire coal at Harborough and transporting the local merchandise for distribution in northern parts.[2] On their side, the LNU looked after the comfort of potential users of the wharf by building an inn, the Union (now the Six Packs) which opened in April 1810.[3] A warehouse block was erected on the wharf, and was ready for letting by October 1810, although it seems that at first there was some difficulty in finding a tenant.[4] There was a 'great influx' of teams from the surrounding district, and the company found it necessary to build a stable for their accommodation. The committee members rubbed their hands at the prospects—not only was the GU under construction, but other new canals—the Peak Forest, Chesterfield, Cromford, and others—promised to bring traffic to the LNU and fulfil its 'hopes . . . so long deferred'. With the canal works still being paid for (even after the opening, there was still much work to be done on the summit pound, including gravelling 3 miles of towpath and some 'bottoming') their expenditure continued to exceed income: in the first half year of 1810, receipts were £2,394 against expenses of £3,513. But the company was nearly out of the wood. Not so one of its early stalwarts; the unfortunate Dr Bree had rashly taken more shares than his means could justify, and owed no less than £2,182. The company, happily, no doubt recognising the part he played in the project's early years, was not hard, allowing him to pay off in easy stages, and even draw his dividends despite the debt, when the time came for dividends to be declared. He seems to have cleared off his debt in 1817.

With trade growing steadily, the committee sought to encourage a brisk rate of turnover at its wharfs by imposing a tariff for wharfage and warehousing, the favourable rate of 4d per ton for up to 28 days being given to coal and coke and one or two other commodities whose sale the company wished to promote, as against the 6d per ton charged on most goods. A stiff rate of 6d per bottle or carboy was imposed on dangerous materials such as aqua fortis and oil of vitriol, to induce their owners to remove them from the company's premises speedily.[5] The firm of Ella, Coleman & Co instituted a weekly boat service between Leicester and Harborough, the boat reaching Harborough wharf on Monday evening and returning to Leicester on Thursday morning. The company's finances reflected the improved position: the chairman, Paget, was able to report to the General Assembly on 18 November 1811 that the income, £3,001 comfortably exceeded the expenditure, £1,826. At the next General Assembly, on 18 May 1812, the income was even better, £4,573, although expenses had risen, too, being £2,776. It would have been possible to pay a £2 per share dividend; but the General Assembly accepted the committee's recommendation that the surplus should be invested instead, and Exchequer Bills were bought. The proprietors' self-denial was rewarded at the next General Assembly, when continuing improvement—receipts £3,955, expenditure £1,349—led to the declaration of the company's first dividend, at the rate of £2 per share.[6] At the same time, the General Assembly, no doubt satisfied with the capable way in which the committee was guiding the concern, authorised it to vary the rates of tolls imposed by the LNU as it thought fit, a resolution which was repeated regularly by successive General Assemblies with very little questioning. It was a wise move: troubled times lay ahead of the LNU, and when the time came to fight rivals for its trade, the committee's hand was strengthened by its ability to make immediate decisions about rates, the more so since it also had to carry with it five other companies on the Leicester line.

During the period when the company's finances were still in doubt, the staffing and organisation of the concern were reviewed. The General Assembly, as is the wont of such bodies, attributed the large expenditure to overstaffing and inflated salaries, and called for cuts all round, against the committee's advice. It did not always succeed. As early as 1810, it ordered the dismissal of James King, the assistant of Breedon, the engineer, and that of Sheppard, the pay clerk. King was indeed dismissed, but a few months later, the two clerkships of the company were combined, and Sheppard, described as 'the accountant', became sole clerk, a post he held with credit until 1848. The LNU made a considerable saving on this, for Sheppard was paid £40 per annum for what the two clerks previously had received £60 per annum each. The unfortunate Sheppard, who continued to hold the post of accountant as well as clerk, suffered a further indignity in 1812, when his pay was cut again to 30 guineas (£31.50) per annum. With the steady improvement of the company's position, his salary was restored to £40 in the following year, and to £60 in 1827. King was still in the company's service, at Debdale wharf, in 1813.[7] He was probably there much later, too, for his son was allowed to take over the warehouse at Debdale on the same terms as 'his late father' in 1847. George Smith, superintendent of the line of extension, was not so lucky. At first, he escaped with a pay cut on account of 'illness and falling off' from 2 guineas (£2.10) to 1 guinea (£1.05) a week. But the General Assembly on 18 November 1811 ordered him to be dismissed with a gratuity of 20 guineas (£21). Breedon, the engineer, did not get off scot free, but at least he had the promise of better things, for £40 per annum was stopped from his salary until the GU should open.

As the GU progressed towards completion, the committee set to work putting its line into order to cope with the anticipated influx of through traffic between the Midlands and the south. In 1813, traffic on the summit pound was stopped for some six weeks while four miles—presumably from Kibworth top lock to Foxton—were cleaned out, and probably deepened, for it was claimed that the work would increase the pound's capacity as a reservoir. Although the extra expense which this incurred swallowed up so much of the income as to preclude the payment of a dividend for the second half year of 1813, income, too, rose, and the company finished up comfortably on the right side, income being £3,478, against an expenditure of £2,818; the surplus was invested in Exchequer Bonds. The committee was able to dispose of a further £1,000 in the same way in 1814, despite a slightly lower tonnage return due to bad weather. In July 1814, a deputation from the committee attended a meeting of representatives of the GJ, GU, Loughborough, Erewash, and Cromford companies to discuss methods of persuading the Derbyshire coalowners, who at the time sent their coal to London chiefly by way of Gainsborough and the sea, to use the Leicester line instead in view of the imminent opening of the GU. But as happened all too often, efforts at co-operation were nullified by one company remaining out of step. In this case, the assembled delegates agreed to an all-round toll reduction, but the Leicester Navigation, not represented at the conference, refused, and the plan failed. Toll reductions or not, some traders at least were preparing to develop traffic on the new through route. Pickford's took a lease of the LNU's Half Moon wharf, on the east bank of the Soar just below Castle Mill in Leicester and adjoining West Bridge, for 40 years at £80 per annum, in addition to which they were to pay £7½ per cent per annum on the cost of the warehouses the company had built there.[8] Deacon, Harrison, Shenton & Co's fly-boats began carrying on 13 August 1814 from London by way of Leicester to the Midlands and north-west.[9] They sailed three times a week, on Tuesday, Thursday, and Saturday nights.

The coal traffic of which so much had been expected was slow in building up. It received very little in the way of encouragement by reduced tolls from the companies of the new line, although this was in no way due to feet-dragging by the LNU, whose committee sent a plea to the other companies for co-operation in this, stressing that 'they are now and have always been prepared to make any sacrifice'. It had little effect on the comfortably placed navigations north of Leicester, however. One enterprising Derbyshire coalowner, Edward Miller Mundy of Shipley colliery, leased a part of Debdale wharf, and was soon said to be 'establishing a considerable coal trade in Northamptonshire'.[10] To compensate for the disappointing coal traffic returns, the committee sought to encourage trade in Mountsorrel granite, an excellent material for road making. It went quite well, and a steady traffic in this commodity developed, remaining one of the LNU's regular sources of income for many years. The effects can be seen to this day in the numerous yards and back streets in south Leicestershire still surfaced with granite setts. Perhaps it was the finding of this new source of revenue which induced the company on 20 May 1816 to resolve that each proprietor attending a General Assembly should be allowed a bottle of wine at the company's expense. Or it may have hoped to increase the attendance at these meetings, which were held alternately in Leicester and Harborough. If so, the move failed, for not even the prospects of free drinks could persuade the proprietors to take an interest in their own business: the average number present at Assemblies continued to be about 22 people, of whom over half were committee members.

The company now settled down to a quiet period of steady, if modest, prosperity. Income regularly exceeded expenditure in the proportion of approximately three to one, and a dividend of £2 per share was paid each half year on all but five occasions, when no dividend was paid, between 1815 and 1835, representing an annual dividend of approximately 5 per cent on the paid-up shares. Expenditure, apart from maintenance, took the form of improvements to meet increasing traffic demands—as when additional stables were built at the Union Inn, Market Harborough, in 1821, and a new warehouse at the wharf there in 1824. An additional basin was constructed at Harborough in 1825. Like other navigations, the LNU had trouble with millers on its river section, and was driven in 1818 to buy Crow Mills, near Blaby, a windmill being included in the sale as well as the watermill, for £900, although it only seems to have paid £850 for them in the end. These proved expensive, necessitating a good deal of expenditure in the way of repairs; over £930 were spent on them in the next 4 years.

From the middle 1820s, efforts were being made to revive and extend activity in the Leicestershire coalfield, whose trade had been badly hit when Leicester had been opened up to the Derbyshire coal trade with the completion of the Leicester Navigation in 1794. The committee of the LNU, seeing the possibility of another source of traffic for its canal, sought to encourage these endeavours, and ordered £2,000 to be sent as a gift to one of the companies prospecting in the area. Which one is not said, but within the next few years, new seams were to be found at several places in west Leicestershire—Ibstock, Bagworth, Whitwick, Snibstone—and the pits at Coleorton, closed down since the late eighteenth century, were to be reopened; the committee's forecast was to be proved accurate. The search for coal culminated in the promotion of a railway, the Leicester & Swannington, from the coalfield to the very bank of the canal in Leicester. Although the project had been discussed as early as 1825, it was not until 1828 that a definite proposal came before the public, and the LNU warmly supported it. The company leased 3,890sq yd of land in the Augustine Friars, Leicester, to the railway company in 1832, and sold the land to it in 1835. It also laid a siding from the railway into its own wharf, building four offices for the use of traders there. The committee also looked ahead to a further growth of traffic, and took a lease of more land adjoining.

The railway opened to Bagworth in 1832, and throughout in 1833. At first, the LNU's share of its traffic was disappointing: the new pits were hardly yet in full production, and the greater part of their output was taken by the townsfolk of Leicester (one witness mentions as many as fifty carts waiting at the West Bridge station to load when the coal train arrived, all existing stocks having been cleared out). But when the early teething troubles were surmounted, the LNU's revenue began to increase satisfactorily, as the following table, in which shillings and pence have been omitted for the sake of clarity, will show:

	Income	*Expenditure*
	£	£
1832	8,659	2,650
1833	9,242	3,099
1834	9,998	2,818
1835	11,476	2,957
1836	15,120	3,265
1837	15,682	3,609

Unfortunately, traffic to individual wharfs and through traffic returns are not available for these crucial years, but when they commence, in 1843, it is quite clear that, as would be expected, the bulk of the profits came from the latter; even with the substantial drawbacks allowed to traders, the tonnages on through traffic were more than double those on the company's busiest wharf, Harborough, and were not far from being half the total receipts from the traffic of the whole canal. They reached their highest point in 1847, when receipts from the wharfs on the LNU were already declining, the revenue from through traffic being £15,100 against a total of £3,453 from the combined traffic of Market Harborough, Great Bowden, Debdale, and Kilby Bridge (Blaby had been leased to a trader); of this latter figure, Harborough returned £2,613, a measure of the relative insignificance of the LNU's local traffic even before serious railway competition began. It is doubtful whether the committee made any serious attempt to encourage it. Traders at Harborough, in fact, took the view that it did the opposite, in that drawbacks were given to coal passing through the canal but not to that delivered locally, and in 1841 they took the company to court over this, though unsuccessfully.

At about this time, too, the LNU itself took legal action—against a rival of dangerous potential, the Midland Counties Railway, which opened its line from Nottingham and Derby to Rugby via Leicester in 1840. On 24 November 1840, the viaduct carrying the railway over the LNU near Crow Mills collapsed, traffic on the canal being stopped for some eight weeks.[11] The LNU in due course sued the MCR, and was awarded £170 damages.

THE YEARS OF DECLINE (1847–63)

Looking back on the company's recent history at the end of 1847, an LNU shareholder would have had every reason to be content. No half yearly meeting since 1833 had failed to declare a dividend of at least £2 per share, usually more, and on several occasions it had been as much as 3 per cent—with, in addition, a 15s (75p) bonus per share for the sale of land to the L & SR in 1835, and a £1 bonus (because the committee really did not want to keep too much money in the reserve account!) in 1837. But the company had reached its zenith; ahead of it lay only decline and falling receipts. This had already begun at its own wharfs: 1844 was the high-water mark at Market Harborough and Debdale, receipts being respectively £3,153 and £532. By 1850, Harborough was down to £1,736, Debdale to £342. Kilby Bridge fluctuated—in fact, it had its best year in 1849, with a return of £338, but this was exceptional, and the general trend there was downwards, too. The true position, however, was masked by the fact that through traffic continued to increase until 1847, which year also saw a sudden and short-lived increase in trade at both Harborough and Debdale, the former managing to produce good returns until it delined rapidly after 1849. In that year, tonnages returned in respect of Harborough were £2,806; in 1852, they were £964, and never again did they achieve four figures—in fact, in 1861 they fell to £80, and only twice (in 1866 and 1867) returned to three figures during the period for which detailed statistics are available.

If the decline of local trade was rapid, the collapse of through traffic was dramatic. In 1847, this returned the handsome figure of £15,100; in 1848, this fell to £6,957. It continued to fall with little pause, most steeply from £4,624 in 1854 to £3,422 in 1855, and steadying somewhat in the 1860s before beginning a new and slower (there was so much less trade to lose now) decline in 1867. As early as 1839, the committee had foreseen that railway competition must inevitably eat into their 'merchandize' traffic, and had attempted to build up and keep their coal trade. But it can hardly have anticipated anything so disastrous as this, and spoke bitterly of the 'almost Imperial powers' granted to the railways.

There are, however, difficulties in the way of equating the decline of trade on the LNU exclusively with the growth of the railway system in the area (though the railway was at the back of most of their troubles—eg the fall in trade in 1848 may be due to some considerable extent to the abandonment by Pickford's of canal carrying in favour of rail in 1847, as mentioned below). Market Harborough wharf had its best years in 1843 and 1844, and traffic declined thereafter, though it is true that this was more rapid after 1849, the year in which the first railway arrived in Harborough, the LNWR Rugby–Stamford branch, which may have introduced Warwickshire coal as a competitor to water-borne Leicestershire and Derbyshire. The Midland Railway's main line from Leicester to Hitchin via Harborough was opened in 1857, by which time the wharf's trade was a mere ghost of its former self, but it helped in the general rout of the LNU: Market Harborough's 1857 return of £480 became a paltry £182 in 1858, and by 1869 it was returning less than Kilby Bridge (£88 against the latter's £170). Earlier, the Midland had aimed a blow at the company's through traffic when, in 1849, it opened a branch from its main line at Knighton, just south of Leicester, to the L & SR (which it had bought) at Desford Junction. Coal from the Leicestershire pits could now travel all the way to London by rail, instead of being transhipped to boats at West Bridge. In 1854, 1,167 tons of coal from the Coalville area reached London by canal, compared with 2,939 tons by rail. The amount of trade lost to the canal is further shown by the figure of 54,797 tons of coal sent in the same year by the Butterley Company alone over the LNWR to London; before the Railway Age, this would have gone by water, much of it by the Leicester line. It is likely that even more Leicestershire coal would have gone by rail if the railways could have taken it (though a conference of canal companies in March 1860 heard from 'the Shipley and other Derbyshire coal Companies' that the latter preferred to send some coal by water despite slightly lower railway rates, because it arrived in better condition than the railway-borne coal, and because they did not want to come wholly under the power of the railways. Moreover, until the opening of the Hitchin line, there were many complaints of delays to MR coal trains at the point where they passed on to the LNWR, Rugby. The Hitchin line, too, was not free from delays, and it may be that one of the reasons why the decline of the LNU's traffic, checked in the early 1860s, began again in 1867 was the opening of the MR's own London extension.

That there was a tremendous falling off of trade after 1847 is evident, not only from the sharp decrease in receipts, but from a statement of Thomas Grahame of the GU that in 1849 the number of boats passing Foxton locks was 30,763, while in 1857 it had dwindled to 15,780. Unfortunately, it is seldom that traffic on the LNU can be tied down to quantities in terms of

Page 89

Foxton locks from the air. Note the passing pound separating the upper and lower staircases of locks; lock-keeper's house at top of flight; houses for toll collector (left) and lock carpenter at bottom; side ponds, central ones much reduced in size by the works of the incline; upper approach arm to incline, now overgrown; traces of masonry in the scrub covering the site of the incline—these represent the abutments of the southern ramp and the base of the engine house; lower arm to incline, now a boat mooring

Page 90 (*above*) Bosworth tunnel, south portal; (*below*) Crick tunnel, south portal

tons or boats at this period, since the committee was content to study tonnage returns, which show the amount of cash received by the company each month in the form of tolls. This is important, because tolls, and therefore tonnages, were varied from time to time, so that the same quantity of goods could be represented by different sums of money at different times. During this period, the committee had not only to vary the tolls to keep what trade the canal had and to attract back some that it had lost, but even, especially at first, before the implications of railway competition dawned upon the northern canals of the line, who had prospered so easily and for so long, to dissuade these latter from actually increasing the tolls.[12]

At first, the LNU had ideas of using the Midland Counties Railway as a feeder, in the same way as the L & SR had served it. In 1843, in reply to a query, the committee offered to make a basin at Crow Mills, where the MCR line from Leicester to Rugby crossed the canal, if the railway company would make a wharf, so that coal could be transferred from rail to boat there, and to reduce the toll on coal to London from the intended wharf from 1s 9d (9p) to 1s 3d (6p). The MCR had other ideas, and nothing came of it, though the possibility of a wharf here was considered again later.[13] As yet, the LNU regarded its position as strong, and it refused to lower tonnages on coal bound for the GJ in 1843 and 1844. But in 1845 it changed its tune, and, at the instigation of the GJ, its rates began to fall. The overall tonnage on coal passing to the GJ went down from 1s 9d (9p) to 10¾d, while coal loaded for wharfs on the LNU paid 2¼d per ton per mile; at the same time, the wharfage charge was lowered from 4d to 2d per ton. Shortly after, coal for the GU beyond Bosworth tunnel had 6d (2½p) per ton knocked off the tonnage. Other goods benefited, too: merchandise between Leicester and London was to pass at 5½d per ton, and all goods to and from the GU paid 1d per ton per mile from or to any wharf on the LNU.

On 15 October 1847, the committee received very bad news: Pickford's, the great canal carrying firm, had decided to abandon canal carrying in favour of railways, and gave notice to quit the LNU's Half Moon wharf, Leicester.[14] Maybe the committee had foreseen this possibility, or received advance warning unofficially, for in the previous year they had reduced the rent £10 per annum, perhaps hoping to induce Pickford's to stay on. Clearly, Pickford's would take their regular trade with them, and it was imperative that the LNU should attract it back. The committee therefore decreed, at the meeting which accepted Pickford's notice, that the tonnage on coal for the GJ should be 10¾d per ton, but that if it went on to the Oxford Canal, or to Paddington, Brentford, or places south, a drawback of 4¾d should be allowed; it would thus pay 6d (2½p) for the 19 miles of the LNU over which it passed. Next month, the General Assembly accepted an agreement negotiated with the GJ, which was preparing to operate its own carrying department, under which, for a period of twenty-one years or as much of that time as the GJ operated on the LNU as carriers, tonnage on all goods but coal and coke passing any distance was not to exceed 6d (2½p) per ton, that between the GU and Harborough 2d per ton. Coal tonnage was not to exceed 10¾d. In return the GJ was not to charge more than the lowest tolls on any coal coming on to its canal from outside the Leicester line, and in any case not more than ½d per ton per mile.

The fall in trade must have been greater than the committee had feared (through traffic in February 1847 returned £1,086, in February 1848 £725), for as early as February it was considering fresh arrangements, and in May an agreement was made with the GJ—which had not yet started carrying coal—by which tonnage was replaced by a boatage charge of 8s (40p) a boat, when two boats travelled together, on coal for London. Mountsorrel granite to the GJ was to pay 4½d per ton, and boats carrying it could return with a load of manure at a boatage charge of 3s 2d (16p). The GJ on its side was not to charge more than 8s 9d (44p) for freightage and tonnage on its line, and this was to include the 1s 1d (5½p) London toll (traders passing more than 6 boatloads a week received a further bonus, being charged a maximum of 8s 6d (42½p) on the GJ). The coal was to be delivered to the merchant's wharf, and he was to be allowed 7 days to unload it without being charged demurrage. The agreement was to run for 7 years at most.[15] There was a snag: the GJ could not at that moment provide enough boats for the trade, and as a result of complaints from merchants, a reduction of 3¾d per ton on London-bound coal in other traders' boats had to be allowed.

It was all in vain. For a time, the falling off of through traffic was checked at a much lower level, but it never showed any serious signs of recovery, and dwindled again from the middle 1850s. By this time too, the committee had awakened to the fact that its local trade was threatened. During the Railway Mania of the 1840s, a scheme had been authorised for a railway passing through the LNU's territory, parallel to it in places, and, although economics and railway politics had combined to prevent its being made at that time, it was obvious that the plan would eventually be taken up again. The committee therefore conducted an experiment at Harborough: they appointed a subcommittee to enter the coal trade on the company's behalf at that wharf. As a result, it was able to report to the General Assembly on 22 November 1848 that the company had made a profit of £1 7s 1½d (£1.35½)—trifling, as the committee said, but it brought the price of coal in Harborough down from 16s 4d (81½p) to 14s (70p) per ton. The venture was therefore continued on a larger scale, and, in addition, extended to Kilby Bridge from 1 January 1850. As an additional incentive to local trade, tonnage on coal to Harborough was reduced to 1s 2d per ton (6p), and to the wharfs at Great Bowden, Gallow Hill, Foxton, Debdale, and Wistow Lane to 1s (5p), in April. The feared scheme for a railway from Wigston via Harborough to Bedford and Hitchin (where it was to join the Great Northern Railway's main line, thus making another through route to London) was duly revived by the MR, and the committee, having made a predictably futile appeal for an agreement between the railway company and the LNU for traffic to Harborough, began once more to adapt the rates to the changed circumstances. Having persuaded the northern canals of the line to make reductions, it finally (after a subcommittee had held 'two protracted meetings'), established the following rates: to Aylestone (4 miles) 2d; Blaby (6 miles, formerly 3d) 3d; Kilby Bridge (9 miles, 6d) 4d; Wistow Lane (13 miles, 9d) 4d; Debdale (17 miles, 9d) 4¼d; Foxton (19 miles, 9d) 4¾d; Gallow Hill (21 miles, 9d) 5¼d; Great Bowden (22 miles, 9d) 5½d; Market Harborough (24 miles, 9d) 6d.

The rate to Harborough was reduced even further in 1860, when a conference of the Leicester line canals, making a bid to retain their traffic to Harborough and Northampton, agreed to a further reduction of 2d per ton, the LNU thus allowing a distance of 24 miles for 4d. This seems to have been one of the few occasions when the MR became seriously worried by its canal rivals, but a combination of threats and persuasion, coupled with the desertion of the Loughborough and Erewash canals, always liable to be lukewarm towards the common cause, led to the withdrawal of the reduction.

The LNU was always ready to answer appeals by other canals for toll modifications. Its even more hard-pressed neighbour, the GU, wrote in 1851 asking for reductions in coal tariffs to meet competition from the Rugby & Stamford railway at its wharfs, and the LNU duly obliged by lowering its rates to 1s (5p) per ton on coal delivered short of Bosworth tunnel, 9d beyond it, rather to the GJ's annoyance. It also made reductions on coal for Aylesbury and Buckingham, following a conference of canal companies headed by the GJ. Individual traders, too, were listened to sympathetically. For example, Finney & Seale guaranteed to send a minimum of 10,000 tons of coal over the LNU in one year, and were allowed a drawback of 3d per ton in return. There were several instances of quite small traders getting similar concessions.

One branch of trade which never lived up to hopes placed on it was that of the transport of cattle and sheep to London. This scheme was largely a brain child of Thomas Grahame, one-time chairman of the GJ, and prominent on both GU and LNU. His view was that the canals had little hope of getting back the trade they had lost to the railways, and that it would be more sensible to look for new lines than to indulge in futile competition. He first brought the matter up in 1850. No action was taken, however, until 1852, by which time the plan had come to include passengers too. Boats engaged in the trade were to be allowed the rate of 2d per boat per mile, to be limited to 6 pairs of boats weekly, and it was hoped that the trade would begin within 8 months. The GJ, however, raised objections, to the anger of Grahame, who suspected them of wanting to make a separate arrangement with 'our rivals of the rail'. Eventually the GJ gave way, but nothing further seems to have happened. As late as January 1858, Grahame was still urging the desirability of the trade on the several companies, and had approached traders who expressed interest, but he admitted that it would necessitate a large outlay on new boats, and the scheme probably came to grief on this. Bringing new traffic on to the canals was one of Grahame's objects in advocating this scheme; but he had another—to encourage canal companies to make such general agreements as this, based on a fixed mileage rate applicable to all, as a weapon against their competitors. Clearly he had seen the weak point of the Leicester line, the lack of a single policy of rate assessment on the whole distance, and regarded this plan as a step towards a solution.

THE LINE, ITS STAFF AND ORGANISATION, 1809–63

Grahame was the one outstanding personality of this period, at least in the direction. The chairmanship down to 1835 was largely monopolised by the bankers, Thomas Paget and his son, another Thomas. For a period between 1808 and 1816, in most recent years the chairmanship at the General Assemblies alternated, Paget usually chairing the May meeting in Harborough, while first Richard Gresley, then Henry Wood, chaired the November one in Leicester. The committee complained of the expense of the meetings thus alternating between the two towns. Not until November 1837, however, was the practice established of holding all General Assemblies in Leicester, at first at the Bell or the Saracen's Head, then, as the company became poorer, in their clerk's office, first in Horsefair Street, then at 23 Friar Lane. The scheme of alternating chairmen was finally abandoned in 1822, and Paget junior retained sole occupation of the chair until 1835. His successor, Charles Robinson, held office until 1848, having the singular good fortune to coincide with the maximum, and last, period of the company's prosperity—to some at least of which he contributed, if the sentiments expressed by the committee, and the piece of plate worth 100 guineas (£105) they presented to him, on his retirement are to be believed. From 1839 to 1846, there was a reversion to the practice of alternating chairmen for the Assemblies—Robinson chaired the November meetings, and William Evans Hutchinson those in May. Despite the continually worsening position of the LNU, its chairmen did not fly from the struggle too precipitately. Robinson's successor, John Pinfold Stallard, held office until his death in 1853, recorded by the committee with 'deep sorrow' as 'the death of an old friend'. He was followed by Joseph Johnson, who retired in 1857, having served on the committee since the good days of 1843. William Weston Stretton, who followed, had been on the committee since as long ago as 1838, and occupied the chair until a well-earned retirement in 1869. It will thus be seen that the company's difficulties were in no way due to lack of experience among the men at the top.

Long service was common among the officers, too. Sheppard, the clerk, who had suffered such indignities during the years of struggle, lived to see himself recorded in the minutes as 'our respected Clerk, who has faithfully and efficiently served the Company for nearly half a century' and pensioned off at £60 per annum in 1848, but died in 1849. As well as being a watershed in the company's history, 1848 was a year of farewells to old servants—John Linthwaite, the Leicester toll collector, retired on a pension of £1 per week, and a similar sum was voted to the retiring wharfinger at Harborough, John Green, who had been with the company more than 40 years. Green's letter of thanks, referring to 'the Kindness and Courtesy with which you have always treated me' was more than a polite formality, for the committee had in recent months taken violent exception to the behaviour of Green's son, who helped him at the wharf, ending by giving Green junior marching orders; as their action over the pension and Green's letter show, the committee members did not allow their anger with the son to affect the father.

The integrity of the committee is also shown with regard to the clerkship, when Sheppard's successor, Lawton, died after only a year in office. There were several candidates for the post, and the committee, on the grounds that they knew several of the candidates personally, passed the election of his successor on to the General Assembly without making any recommendation; the upshot being that William Palmer was elected on 20 May 1850. He served until he gave up his legal practice in 1857, being succeeded by Harry James Davis.

Quite the most distinguished record of service to the LNU is that of the appropriately-named George Foxton who became surveyor to the company in 1837, and was responsible for the upkeep of the canal and operational matters for the next thirty years. He lived at the company's house at Kilby Bridge, where he developed the coal trade already mentioned, and evidently traded on his own account too. In 1867, he retired, and was immediately elected to the committee. In 1869 he became chairman, and held the office until his death in 1877.

On 9 April 1858, a subcommittee appointed to review the company's affairs with a view to economies submitted its report to the committee, and the state of the organisation as revealed in that report may fittingly sum up the result of the events recounted in this chapter.[16] The subcommittee felt that the salary of the surveyor, raised to £200 per annum in 1840, might well be cut in the very different circumstances of 1858, especially as he did not now devote his whole time to LNU work (Foxton replied that he had reduced the company's expenditure greatly, and this certainly seems justified by the figures; expenses had fallen from £2,706 in 1848, to £1,666 in 1858). The £40 per annum salary of the toll collector at Foxton could also be cut, as he had much less to do since traffic had fallen off, and in any case he was largely only a check on the Leicester man. There were seven lock-keepers, but one had recently died, and he was not to be replaced, saving £40 per annum and a cottage. There was also a vacancy among the labourers, and not filling this would save £37. The Kibworth lock-keeper rented 2 acres of land from the company, and this might be sold. The committee duly cut £50 from Foxton's salary, and halved that of the unfortunate Atkins, toll collector at Foxton, leaving him with a mere £20. (In 1862, Foxton offered, 'in view of the present state of the business of the Canal' to take a further cut to £120 per annum, to be restored when finances justified it, a gesture accepted by the committee with gratitude. The idea thus being put into the heads of the committee members, next month they reduced the salary of Ruffell, the Leicester toll collector, from £110 to £100 per annum.

The company's wages bill was not large by any standards, but economies were made, reducing it from a weekly average of about £22 in 1851 to £16 in 1862. When Astley, wharfinger at Leicester, died in 1861, his successor, Joseph Nokes, received only £1 per week (Astley had been paid £1 6s (£1.30)). (As a matter of interest regarding the sources of recruitment of canal workers, Nokes—aged 30, 'Married?—Not yet' as he told the committee—was an upholsterer by trade, and got the job in preference to a grocer, a clerk in a tax office, and a book-keeper.) Men going sick were required to provide a substitute and pay his wages themselves, though poor Astley, for a period of sick leave in his last years, was allowed to pay only half. There was no question of substantial pensions now. Yet some of the old patriarchal relations between the committee and its servants survived; when a new lock-keeper had to be appointed to replace John Peberdy at Leicester, Foxton was ordered not to dismiss Peberdy, an 'old and faithful servant of the Company' who was past his work, but to keep him on to do odd jobs at 9s (45p) per week.

The long decline of the LNU inevitably makes sad reading, but the story had lighter moments. One of these occurred in 1852, when the long established custom of the townsfolk of Leicester of bathing in the river Soar, on a section which was part of the LNU's line, gave rise, or so the committee said, to complaints of bathers 'wantonly exposing their persons' and indulging in 'other unseemly behaviour' apparently too shocking to be recorded, which the committee found 'grossly insulting' to the exceptionally modest boatwomen passing along the LNU. The committee therefore sent a letter to the town clerk demanding that he put a stop to the practice, or the company would forbid bathing in the river altogether. The town clerk soothingly replied that he had placed the matter before the magistrates, who would do what they could, as they would be sorry to see bathing, 'so beneficial to the working classes', stopped; but they feared that it would not be possible to save the virtuous boatwomen from 'the annoyance of seeing the other sex in a somewhat exposed condition'. Nor was it. Not content with running about with nothing on, some bathers in 1857 tipped a loaded coal boat up. The magistrates shrugged the matter off as not within their jurisdiction. The furious committee gave the owner of the coal £1 towards his his expenses, and the boatwomen had to go on putting up with the sight of the sons of Leicester naked and unashamed.

THE HARBOROUGH AND STAMFORD CANAL PROJECTS

The vicissitudes experienced by the LNU in its progress to its eventual termination at Harborough seem to have cured it of all desire to extend its line in other directions, but it was always ready to listen to would-be promoters planning to make canals to join up with it, and to give all help which did not involve spending money. The area to the east attracted such speculators. Even at the outset, as we have seen, the folk of Uppingham and Kettering were anxious to have a connection with the LNU. Nothing came of this, but a more ambitious scheme, for a canal from Stamford to the LNU, haunted the district for many years.

The first mention of the idea in the public press occurs in 1809, when it seems to have arisen at the same time as a rival plan to link Stamford with the Oakham Canal. This latter project, ultimately known as the Stamford Junction, was adopted at a meeting in Stamford on 5 September 1809, and involved the creation of a line of waterway from Oakham via Stamford to Lynn and Boston. Telford was to be asked to do a survey, but as time was getting on if the promoters wished to go to Parliament for an Act in the next session, they adopted, for the time being, a plan already made by Robert Whitworth.[17] On 23 September 1809, supporters of the rival scheme, for a canal from the LNU to Stamford, met and ordered a survey to be made. This project had powerful official backing, the mayor of Stamford (who was in the chair) and the Recorder both being on the committee. Over a hundred people were present, and fifty put their names down for shares on the spot. There was a link with the LNU in George Wartnaby, who became the project's Harborough solicitor, as he was already the LNU's.[18] Bevan, who was once more faced with a delicate situation in his relationship with his profession's leader, Telford, was called in to act as engineer to the new scheme. Having examined the region, Bevan reported to a meeting in early December that a line from the LNU near Great Bowden to cross the Welland between that place and Sutton, and thence run south of the river to Stamford, was practicable, involving a canal some 25½ miles long with 92ft of lockage, the cost probably being £103,010. Subscriptions for the greater part of this were enrolled at once, and the promoters made a £2 per cent call on the £100 shares, which were soon at a premium. The *Northampton Mercury* said that the promoters would have had no difficulty in raising twice the necessary sum.[19] This seems to have been literally true, for at a meeting on 26 February, the mayor again in the chair, it was ordered that no more subscriptions should be taken, as they had enough money already, merely reserving shares to the value of £10,000 for the landowners on the line.[20] This, though they had increased the potential cost of their scheme by agreeing to extend it east of Stamford to serve Spalding, Lynn, Wisbech, and Boston.[21] Spalding agreed to back the scheme against a plan of Telford's for a Stamford to Spalding canal (Bevan and Telford seemed fated to clash, to the latter's discomfort, everywhere).[22] The LNU resolved unanimously to give the scheme 'collectively and individually, the most strenuous support', not that this meant a great deal. Both the GJ and the GU promised support, too.[23] All seemed set fair for the promoters.

But this was the pinnacle of their success. Henceforth, all went awry. The root cause seems to have been their failure to convince the landowners. It is probably not without significance that, whereas the project was largely the work of the civic and professional men of Stamford, the rival Stamford Junction Canal was chaired by Gerard Noel Noel, a prominent landowner in the Rutland–Northamptonshire area. The first signs of formidable opposition came at a meeting at Kettering—which years before had been so keen to get a canal link with the LNU—on 14 November 1810. Reports are as conflicting as usual, but it seems that as many as two-thirds of the landowners on the line of the intended Harborough–Stamford canal may have been present: one report quotes eighty-four as attending, of whom sixty voted to oppose the scheme. The grounds given for opposition were that the canal, running parallel to the river for much of its length, would ruin the rich meadow land for which the Welland valley was famous.[24]

Opposition grew. Meetings at Northampton and Peterborough both passed resolutions against the project, the former twice. A further meeting at Kettering reaffirmed its hostility and set up a fund to combat the scheme at the very time the LNU committee was gleefully telling its proprietors of the benefits the scheme would bring.[25] Individuals, too, were taking up arms against it. The scheme did, in fact, contain features well adapted to make enemies. Apart from the main line, which was to leave the LNU a short distance north of Great Bowden wharf, cross the Welland, and virtually follow that river to Stamford, where it joined it, there were two feeders, one from the direction of Husbands Bosworth where there were to be two reservoirs adjacent to each other, the other from West Langton, where a third reservoir was planned—Bevan was always cautious about water supplies. This upset landowners in the area so much that one of them, the Reverend James Ord, of West Langton Hall, went to the expense of having a map engraved to show the effect the reservoir would have on his estate—of its 100 acres, 80 were his—with a statement of his grievances. Some were reasonable: the plan would take all his meadow land. Others were less charitable than might have been hoped for from a cleric: 'disorderly persons' would flock to West Langton for the poaching.[26] Unlike the GU, the Harborough & Stamford had no London influence and experience to help them overcome the opposition; and the project failed.

It was revived in 1814, again with Bevan as engineer. The principal question at issue was the drainage of the lands adjoining the Welland, but Bevan sought to convince a meeting at Kettering on 22 June that the plan for this could be combined with a navigation without any harm. He seems to have failed, for no more is heard of the suggestion.[27]

Once more the idea was revived, in 1823, and by the LNU. The General Assembly in November 1823 resolved that it would be beneficial if the Welland were made navigable from the LNU (they did not say where the connection would be made) to Stamford, and ordered the committee to get in touch with other canal companies about it, and to organise a meeting in Stamford. But once more it lapsed, and the next occurrence of would-be canal promoting in the area was of the old Stamford Junction scheme, from Stamford to Oakham, supported by the

Oakham and Melton Navigation Companies, in 1828. Nothing happened, but in 1830, a real flutter was caused by the appearance of two rival schemes to promote railways between Stamford and Oakham. The LNU committee was ordered to watch the progress of the schemes, and oppose them. Curiously enough, on the very eve of the Railway Age, a last attempt was made to promote a canal from the LNU to Stamford, and in association with a railway company. In May 1837, the LNU General Assembly again voted in favour of supporting a canal on the line of the Harborough & Stamford, and told the committee to do what it could to get it promoted. The committee got Stamford town council interested, and arranged a meeting. The L & SR was also called in, since it was profitably sending coal along the LNU, and would benefit from the more extended market. John Ellis, a member of the committee of the L & SR, arranged a demonstration to convince the men of Stamford: he sent to the mayor, the town clerk, and three leading citizens, 5 hundredweights of 'coals of the best kind we ever saw', intimating that if the canal were built, this coal would be on sale in Stamford very cheaply.[28] The point was taken, and the town council resolved to support the projected canal in every way possible, the mayor putting this into practice by canvassing the landowners for support, with much success. The LNU promised to try to raise capital in their area, if the town council would do likewise.

But it was already too late. A main line of railway was already planned through Leicestershire, and after its completion in 1840, only a few years were to elapse before it threw out a branch which took the trade of the Stamford area for ever away from waterways; and one of its leading promoters was John Ellis.

So Stamford, that loveliest of English towns, never got its canal link with the Midlands, and the LNU never had the chance to swell its revenue by sending Midland coal east, and bringing fenland farm produce west. It is a frustrating story.

CHAPTER 4

The Grand Union Canal, 1814-63

ORGANISATION

UNLIKE the LNU, the GU was a London-biased concern. The activities leading to its construction had been centred on the metropolis; and there was an undoubted gain to the undertaking in being in such close contact with the leaders of the financial world of the day. In particular, its organisation, adapted from that of the GJ, was a more sophisticated thing altogether than that of the LNU, which somehow combined the rustic and the aldermanic. One cannot imagine the London office of the GU omitting, as the provincial firm of solicitors it used for a time did, to invite one of the company's largest shareholders to attend meetings of a committee of which he was a member. On the other hand, the committee members of the LNU had only to walk a few yards from their Leicester offices to reach their canal, and they could visit any part of it in the course of a pleasant half-day on horse-back or in their carriages; while they could meet their employees regularly and keep them up to the mark (a delegation of the GU's subcommittee visited the canal once a year, otherwise there was no contact whatever between the committee and its staff). In the circumstances of the time, these advantages outweighed the benefits of a London-based organisation; but it was to be half a century before the GU realised it.

The headquarters of the company at the time of the opening

was at 10 Norfolk Street, off the Strand, and remained there until 1821, when the GU's poor financial state compelled it to seek smaller premises. Sale, who had been paid as the company's clerk by living rent free in the house, was given an annual salary of 100 guineas (£105) instead, and the company moved to Arundel Street, holding its first meeting there on 4 June 1821. In 1826, it transferred to two rooms in Surrey Street, Strand, next door to the GJ offices, paying a rent of £70 per annum, reduced to £56 in 1845 when one of the rooms was given up as a further economy measure. There were snags: in 1842, the committee determined to give notice, as it feared that the company's property might be endangered by the 'pecuniary difficulties' of the landlady, Mrs Cosier, no doubt expecting that it might find the bailiffs in possession one day—a most embarrassing situation all round, as Cosier was the GU's accountant and was later to be its clerk. But Mrs Cosier's extravagance must have been curbed, for the company stayed on, and when Cosier subsequently moved to 6 Norfolk Street, it went with him, holding its first meeting there on 3 January 1854; the eleven committee chairs and desk, probably nearly all the furniture the company had, were repaired for the transfer, it being too impoverished to buy new equipment by that time. During its stay in Surrey Street, on only two occasions did the committee meet elsewhere. In 1837, Maltby, the then accountant clerk (he had held this office since 1810), was stricken by paralysis, 'which never left him until he died', a few days later, in the company's office, and the company transferred not only a subcommittee meeting but also the General Assembly to 21 Surrey Street, the GJ offices, to avoid disturbing him. The other occasion was in 1838, when, Sale being ill, a meeting was held in his apartment. Having gone to 6 Norfolk Street, the company remained there until it finally moved its headquarters out of London altogether in 1863.

As regards the organisation, this remained the same as had been laid down by the Act and as had built the canal: a General Assembly, electing a General Committee, which in turn appointed the two subcommittees, one dealing with finance (the London Subcommittee) and the other with the managerial aspects of the canal (the Subcommittee in the Country). But the balance of power gradually changed. In the early years, the General Committee was very active, especially on the financial side. As time passed, however, and the early difficulties were at least temporarily overcome and loose ends tied up, the Subcommittee in the Country became increasingly influential (no records of the other subcommittee survive, so it is not possible to say whether this gained in stature too, but it is unlikely). In time, General Committee meetings became much less frequent, and often merely formal gatherings to elect the subcommittees. The General Assemblies never exercised much influence, since they were even worse attended than those of the LNU. Ten or eleven proprietors would have been regarded as a good attendance; it fell to four on at least one occasion. Even for such an important event as the election of a new clerk and a new treasurer in 1863, only seven proprietors turned up, and their combined holding of shares, totalling fewer than 700, forced an adjournment to whip up more support—and at the adjourned meeting, there were still only seven present in person, just enough representation by proxy having been scraped together to give the 700 shares required by the Act to make the meeting effective.[1]

FINANCE

The rejoicings at the opening in August 1814 did not for long conceal the fact that the GU had financial problems. Nevertheless, the committee on 7 September decided optimistically that it would be unnecessary to raise more than was needed to meet immediate requirements, which was £12,000, and it therefore invited subscribers to take part in a two-year loan, at 5 per cent interest, to be repaid at Michaelmas 1816, or converted into GU stock at par, at the option of the creditor. A month later, having found that only £7,000 had been subscribed, it took a more realistic view of the company's financial standing, and ordered

Page 107 (*above*) Original GU milestone, Watford—20 miles from Foxton; (*below*) GJ mile post, near Welford

Page 108
Bridge protection on the GU: (*above*) hard bricks, Watford. An innovation of William Foxton's in 1844; cost 15p; (*below*) guard iron, Crick; cost in 1844, 50p

a reduction of expenses on the line of the canal and the sale of unwanted land. In the following spring, reviewing the company's position, the committee found that 98½ of its shares were unsold, and could only be disposed of at a considerable discount. It owed the treasurer £10,000, and a further £6,000 was owed to contractors and landowners for fencing the canal, damages, and sundry other items. All this could be wiped out by a subscription of £6 per share by the proprietors, and this would also enable the engineer to finish the works, except the raising of the head of the intended reservoir near Naseby—which could wait for the time being, and could be paid for from the sale of the lands at Sulby bought for a reservoir and found unsuitable. This was approved by the General Assembly in June, the subscription to be payable in two instalments of £3 each, at 5 per cent interest. Accordingly, a circular letter setting out details of the scheme, and asking for subscriptions, was sent to the proprietors. They, however, remained unimpressed, despite the threat to go to Parliament for a supplementary Act to enable the company to raise more money if the loan failed, and in a month only £7,564 of the desired £18,904 had been promised. Another circular raised a little more, but on 6 November, £7,539 still remained unsubscribed, and a disgusted committee recorded its reluctance to go to Parliament as being expensive and 'disreputable to the undertaking'. Yet another circular, containing this phrase, was sent to join the bombardment of missives directed at the buttoned-up pockets of the shareholders. Nevertheless, the non-subscribers seem to have been content to wallow in their disreputability, for on 7 February 1816, the committee decided against getting Parliamentary powers to raise the remaining money—it quoted £9,000 as needed, this no doubt being the portion of the two money-raising schemes it had launched which had not been found—as it expected a rise in traffic on account of recent agreements.

The company's financial position did indeed improve henceforward. The loan of £10,000 from Praed, the treasurer, was finally paid off on 30 October 1823. It was not the only time he had come to the rescue financially, and this was appreciated by his colleagues on the committee—when they minuted a waspish resolution that members of the committee whose attendance was irregular should be more 'punctilious' in turning up, he was one of the few specifically excluded from the obligation.[2] The company gave notice that it would pay off all its 5 per cent debts on 25 March 1825, but would renew at 4 per cent if the holders gave due notice. It was consequently faced with having to find £11,978, only a third of the holders having elected to continue at 4 per cent, but Praed's bank came to the committee's aid by offering to hold loan notes presented for payment, at 4 per cent. By 1827, the company felt financially sound enough to declare a first dividend of £1 per share.[3] The treasurer was once more paid off, on 4 January 1828. It was not long, however, before the company was borrowing from him again, and not until 1839 did it finally clear off debts to him once and for all. The GU owed a great deal to Praed, in more senses than one. Not that Praed's attitude was altruistic, but rather one of enlightened self-interest; as a large shareholder in the GJ, it was his concern to get the GU operating efficiently, for the traffic it would bring to that company.

The loan notes were paid off by order of a General Assembly on 24 August 1829, with the usual assistance from the treasurer. After this, the company's other debts were slowly liquidated—an occasional windfall helping, like the sale for £315 of 1½ acres of land alongside Sulby reservoir so that Mrs Payne of Sulby Hall could make a fishpond; the canal was even allowed to draw water from it in an emergency, so long as enough was left for the fish. The debt, £5,226 at the beginning of 1832, was extinguished in 1836, though the company almost at once had to borrow £1,000 from Praed to pay for the New Sulby or Welford reservoir.

During all this time, the company managed from 1827 onwards to pay a dividend of £1 per share on its 2,849½ shares at the June Assembly each year, except in 1833 and 1834, when the bulk of its debts were paid off. In June 1840, it paid £1 5s (£1.25), and in November 1840, its first autumn dividend was declared, 10s (50p) per share. It continued to pay dividends, though small ones, at both Assemblies until 1849, when the only dividend was 17s 7d (87½p), declared at the June General Assembly. It never again paid as much as £1 as a half-yearly dividend; and by the end of this period, it was down to 4s (20p) or 5s (25p). The company's best year was 1846, when it paid £1 5s (£1.25) in June and £1 in November.

From the time when the end of its period of permanent indebtedness was in sight, and there was a possibility of a surplus of cash too small in itself to pay an increased dividend, the company made a practice of buying Exchequer Bills as an investment for its idle money. Frequently these were subsequently sold, but by 1861 the company had amassed them to the amount of £5,000—a sum which may have preserved the concern from bankruptcy in the major structural works which had to be undertaken later. The subcommittee of 25 October 1861, not satisfied that this was the best way for the company to incubate its nest egg, ordered the Bills to be sold, and the money reinvested elsewhere. It took a realistic view of the money market; and in due course, the proceeds from the sale of the Bills were invested by this canal company in—London & North Western Railway debenture stock.

TRAFFIC

One of the features which makes the GU such an attractive waterway today is that it runs through remarkably empty countryside for the whole of its length. This was always recognised, less appreciatively, by the committee, which concentrated its earliest efforts on building up a through trade, especially in coal. This being of such vital importance, the company was prominent in the intricate negotiations between the six concerns on the route between the Derbyshire coalfield and London, though it is fair to the LNU to add that much less is known of the latter company's activities in this field as the committee records do not survive for the crucial early period. But it does seem that the GU was capable of bolder action than its northern neighbour. Needing better water supplies to support an increasing trade, the GU was ready to plunge into debt to have an additional reservoir made.[4] In similar circumstances, the LNU refused even to reduce its tolls, as extra traffic would necessitate spending money on extra water supplies, a remarkably timid philosophy for a canal company.[5]

Water supplies were always a source of concern to the GU, which, as a summit canal, lost water at its northern end to the LNU and its southern end to the GJ, and when the canal opened, the committee had to balance its present inadequacy against trade requirements by judicious manipulation of the rates. It was short of water because the proposed reservoir at Crick had to be abandoned on account of the change of line forced on it by the bad strata on the authorised line of the tunnel; and because the Welford arm, a navigable feeder designed to bring water from two reservoirs (one of which had already been abandoned because of unsuitable ground), was not completed. Even when the new reservoir, at Sulby, was finished or nearly so, matters were set back by the bursting of one of its banks late in the year—on 30 December 1814—due to a sudden thaw, the rush of water causing the Avon to overflow and flood the Stanford area, where two men were drowned. The committee was alarmed, and Bevan had to report on the adequacy of the waste weirs and the stop gate being put in above the lock under construction near Welford mill, in view of the possbility of the Avon embankment being damaged by such a flood.[6] Pending the opening of the Welford arm, coal tonnage was fixed, for boats carrying at least 20 tons, at 1s (5p) per ton beyond Bosworth tunnel but short of the Avon embankment; 1s 6d (7½p) short of Crick tunnel; and 1s 9d (9p) short of Watford locks. The trade going beyond the Avon embankment but not beyond Crick tunnel proved to be disappointingly small, only 40 tons passing on this stretch in 2 months, so the committee raised the toll from 1s 6d (7½p) to 2s (10p) and at the same time ordered that as soon as the Welford arm opened, as far as Welford, the 1s (5p) tonnage on coal should be raised to 1s 6d (7½p).

At first the company sought to overcome the unhelpful attitude of the canals at the northern end of the line by a combination of appeasement and threats. Thus, the Leicester Navigation refusing to lower its tolls to attract coal traffic for the south, the GU asked the LNU to co-operate by joining with them in making the desired reduction from their own tolls instead, and at the same time they offered a 2s (10p) drawback on goods coming to Leicester by land, and thence via the LNU and GU to the south (some of the committee even wanted the GU to abolish all drawbacks on goods which came to them from the Leicester Navigation until the latter saw the error of its ways, but this was rejected). The attempt failed, however, mainly because other companies on the line would not co-operate in reductions, and the GU did not see why it should stand all the loss alone. It tried to put pressure on the northern canals by raising the toll on coal entering the GU from the north to the full parliamentary maximum, so that Staffordshire coal entering from the south could compete (in 1815, coal from the north on to the GU was 4,635 tons; from the south, 1,655 tons). This may have had the immediate effect of raising the GU's receipts; certainly, the general trend was upwards. More important, it jolted the LNU into circularising the other companies, and a scheme for a general toll reduction was drawn up, under which tolls of between two-fifths and three-fifths of the parliamentary maximum were to be charged. It was anticipation of extra traffic created by this new arrangement which led the GU to drop its plans for going to Parliament for an Act to enable it to raise the £9,000 it needed.

The possibility of Staffordshire and Warwickshire coal travelling north along the GU, and even invading south Leicestershire, had been foreseen by some even in the days when the Harborough Navigation had promoted its Northampton extension, but in practice it never amounted to much. Very few returns are available for the GU in its earlier days, but fortunately the coal traffic statements for the 1820s survive, with a breakdown into originating areas:

Year	*Derbyshire* *tons*	*Warwickshire* *tons*
1821	23,220	—
1822	15,324	464
1823	23,190	722
1824	16,459	259
1825	27,352	47
1826	21,391	—
1827	15,196	69
1828	16,800	23

Usually about a quarter to a fifth was for GU wharfs.

An interesting example of the way in which rates and prices could influence local trade occurred in 1822, when Brentnall, the agent of Edward Miller Mundy, the Derbyshire coalowner, wrote saying that the Derbyshire pits had just increased their prices by 3s (15p) per ton, and that competition from Staffordshire coal might be expected as a result.[7] Soon after, the committee received an application from Gilbert, of Bowden wharf on the LNU, asking for a toll reduction on 500 tons of coal he was about to bring from Nuneaton to be landed near Lubenham for sale among the surrounding villages. These were usually supplied from Bowden or Debdale, but the lower price of the Staffordshire coal was causing traffic to flow north instead of south.[8] The coal would probably have been delivered at the rate of a boatload a week, hence no doubt the great increase in receipts from Warwickshire coal in 1823. In 1829, the subcommittee again reduced the toll on coal entering the GU from the GJ to 1s 6d (7½p) per ton to Welford, at the request of Dobson, the owner of a private wharf there, who complained of a great falling off of trade at that place. The company was already very helpful to him, allowing him to pay reduced tolls on lime burnt at Welford and carried back to the LNU in returning coal boats. It also permitted up to 2 tons of packages to pass as general cargo on the top of coal boats to Welford without subjecting the coal to the full rate. But when his successor, Orton, asked in 1832 for a reduction in the tolls on coal from the Oxford Canal, as the northern canals of the line would not give a drawback on coal for Welford, the GU refused, on the grounds that a clause in its Act enabled the LNU to prevent under-cutting in this way. Five years later, Orton won his point when the LNU allowed the GU to lower its rates between Foxton and Welford.

During the rest of the 1830s the canals of the Leicester line continued to haggle about through coal rates more than about any other subject, probably doing more to irritate traders than to help them. Certainly the constantly changing rates must have been a trial to the two toll clerks at Watford and Foxton respectively, who would have needed the courses of training under GJ men at Paddington and Braunston laid on for them by the company, and fully earned their £70 per annum salaries. Even so, the second toll clerk at Watford, William Henfrey, only stuck it for a few months, being appointed on 27 May 1818 and resigning on 3 February 1819. The first man at Foxton, Henry Hollyer, was little better, occupying the position from 1 June 1814 to (probably) early 1818. Their successors, however, were made of sterner stuff. Henfrey was preceded at Watford by John Ruffell, who transferred to the more lucrative post (because of the payment from the LNU for acting as their toll clerk too) at Foxton in 1818 and stayed there until his sudden death in 1843, by which time he was earning £80 per annum from the GU plus £40 from the LNU. When Henfrey resigned from Watford, he was succeeded by Thomas Ratten Atkins, appointed on 3 February 1819, who also was to give the rest of his life to the service of the GU, dying in 1862. On Ruffell's death, Atkins applied to be moved to Foxton, and, after some disagreement, this was granted. The Watford post was given to Ruffell's son Henry, so that whereas before 1844 (when the move was made) there was a Ruffell at Foxton and an Atkins at Watford, after this there was a Ruffell at Watford and an Atkins at Foxton. The Atkins-Ruffell sequence was broken when Henry Ruffell died in 1856 and was succeeded at Watford by John F. Bentley.

The opening of the Leicester & Swannington Railway in 1832 brought another factor into the situation (it also introduced the GU's most unlikely customer, George Stephenson, who, as part owner of Snibstone colliery, applied for and obtained drawbacks on his coal from both the GU and the LNU. For a time, the GU must have been reasonably happy, as coal from both Leicestershire and Derbyshire passed along its line, but as early as 1831 William Jessop (the engineer's son) told the Committee that the Derbyshire coalowners had stated that they would seek to make a railway to Leicester if they could not get better terms from the canals. Although not an immediate threat, it must have been clear that such a line, with its almost certain eventual extension southwards, would be a potential danger to the very insecure prosperity, such as it was, of the GU.

Although coal was foremost in the thoughts of the committee, the latter was active in promoting other traffic as well. An early example was that of gypsum from the Red Hill area on the Loughborough Navigation, for which it reduced the GU rates from 5s (25p) to 2s (10p) per ton, on learning that the pit price of 8s (40p) was increased to 30s (£1.50) by its transportation to market by sea. The LNU's efforts to develop a trade in Mountsorrel granite to London met with a ready response from the GU, which agreed, as part of the attempt to make it possible to sell the granite in London at £1 per ton, to lower the toll from 2s 6d (12½p) per ton to 2s (10p). It also sent a deputation to the GJ committee which persuaded the latter to lower its toll to 3s (15p) and set aside a part of the Great Wharf at Paddington for the granite trade. Further encouragement was given in 1816, when boats which had carried Derbyshire or Leicestershire stone south were to be allowed to return with a cargo of grain tonnage free, though shortly afterwards a register toll of 5s (25p) was imposed on every boat so engaged. It continued to press for a reduction in price, and in 1821, Jackson, owner of the Mountsorrel quarries, quoted 2s 8d (13½p) per ton as his lowest price for granite chippings, 2s 2d (11p) for unbroken granite. This would mean a selling price of 15s 8d (78½p) and 15s 2d (76p) per ton in London. But Sale pointed out that Leith stone cost 7s 6d (37½p) there, Plymouth stone 5s (25p), and Bristol stone 7s 6d (37½p). Jackson offered to lease the quarries to the GU, but the committee understandably refused them. Production of granite was not the purpose of a canal company, although the committee had in 1816 asked a committee member to try to get a 'proper person' used to squaring Aberdeen granite to teach the Leicestershire workmen how to square the Mountsorrel product; the GU was to pay his wages for a fortnight or three weeks.

Despite the cold water its clerk's figures seemed to pour on the possibility of building up a trade in London, the committee persisted. London was, after all, growing at an increasing pace, and the demand for materials for new roads and streets, as well as remaking the old, must have been great. In 1822, the company reduced its tonnage on Mountsorrel granite from 10d to 9d per ton, with the specific intention of competing for the traffic for materials for roads in Highgate and Hampstead. It is not said whether the move was successful, but it seems likely, for in 1832 toll reductions were granted on granite from Lord Stamford's Groby quarries, recently connected with the Leicester line by the opening of the L & SR, and again the committee states that it is to enable the stone to be offered as road material in London.

Other stone, for special purposes, was occasionally allowed reduced tolls. In 1823, a trader applied for a reduced rate for 300,000cu ft of Derbyshire stone for the new London Bridge. The committee agreed, subject to the usual stipulation, that the other canals on the line made reductions too—it may have had some doubts, as the Leicester Navigation only charged 5s (25p) per boatload and the GJ 3s 6½d (17½p) per ton for the whole length of their canals. But the other companies proved amenable, and the stone was allowed to pass the GU at 1s 6d (7½p) per ton. An even more famous national monument owes something to the GU. In 1840, Bolsover stone for the rebuilding of the Houses of Parliament after their destruction by fire in 1834 was going to London by way of the Chesterfield Canal, the Trent, and the sea, the total cost being 14s (70p) per ton. The subcommittee therefore agreed with the other canals on the line to give the stone the same rate as coal for London, which so far as concerned the GU by this time was 9d per ton. The bid was successful, it being reported in May that several freights of the stone had already passed along the canal.

Many other commodities were considered by the committee with a view to attracting their producers to use the Leicester line: timber, grain, flour, bricks (admitted as back-cargo in returning coal and iron boats at 6d per ton), barilla, potash, brimstone, saltpetre, tallow. In 1827 and 1828, it tried to encourage the trade in salt from Droitwich and an unspecified works on the Trent & Mersey Canal, but no more is heard of it later. Where traffic had a choice of waterway, it modified the GU rates to attract it their way. Goods from the Trent & Mersey west of Fradley for LNU wharfs, for instance, were given a substantial drawback to persuade their senders to route them via Braunston and the GU rather than by way of Leicester. In 1838, the committee was peeved with the LNU for refusing to lower its tolls on merchandise generally, and asked the LNU committee to make an exception in favour of Burton ale, as Bass were about to send consignments to London via the Coventry Canal which could be brought on to the Unions' line instead. Such actions without doubt encouraged some firms to send their boats over the GU, for in 1822 Pickford's had drawbacks owing to them from the GU in respect of their trade between Liverpool and Harborough.

Up to the 1830s, the numerous rate changes had been aimed at diverting existing traffic from the roads or other canals on to the Leicester line, or stimulating the growth of new traffic. But with the 1840s, the company went over to the defensive—

to keep as much as possible of what it had by lowering its charges. The committee was quite realistic, not to say pessimistic, about this. It spoke in 1854 of 'low charges alone being likely to retain on the water, the Derbyshire coal traffic, against the despatch, regularity, convenience, and other advantages of the Railway'; the most sanguine railway company prospectus could hardly have put the railways' case better. Curiously enough, the first hint of competition came not from the railway but from the road: in 1828, Deacon & Co put four waggons into service between Leicester and London at canal prices. Pickford's demanded a reduction of toll on these grounds, but the GU, while disposed to co-operate, obviously did not regard the threat as very serious. It was much more alarmed by the 'abrogation' of duty on coal carried coastwise in 1831, and sent representatives to a meeting of Midland coalowners and canal proprietors in Leicester to discuss cuts necessitated by this; but the Leicester delegates were intransigent (they were piqued by the approaching opening of the L & SR) and nothing was done. It was not until 1833 that a reduction satisfactory to all parties was agreed upon (the coalowners contributed by reducing their prices 1s (5p) per ton) but even then 'sea coal' was still cheaper than inland coal in London.[9]

The coming of the railways led among other things to the establishment of a new wharf and new trade on the GU. This was a private venture by a merchant, Jackson of Pimlico, who set up a wharf near Crick railway station, between Norton Junction and Watford locks, in 1841. By 1843, it had passed into the hands of the Clay Cross Colliery Company, whose railborne coal was transhipped to boats here for London, presumably because of the shortage of siding accommodation in that city. For the journey from the wharf to the junction, 1¾ miles, the GU granted a rate of 6d (2½p) per ton. There were some doubts in the GU ranks whether the GU Act authorised them to take any toll at all in this case, as the section in question did not pass a lock, and the solicitors had to report on it.

In 1847, with railway competition eating into the trade of the

Leicester line and Pickford's about to give up carrying by canal, it became essential to take some joint action to shore up the tottering fabric of the line's profitability. Thomas Grahame of the GJ therefore made, on behalf of that company, a proposal to lease the tolls of the canals on the line. The offer to the GU was a rent sufficient to pay its proprietors a dividend of 30s (£1.50) per share per annum, rising to 35s (£1.75) if the GJ ever paid £6 per annum dividend, and £2 if this rose to £7. The GU that year paid £2, in 1848 £1 15s (£1.75), in 1849 17s 6d (87½p), in 1850 £1 10s (£1.50). After that, it never paid more than £1 per annum dividend, and that only in four of the remaining 44 years of its independent existence. But the committee made the wrong guess: it turned down Grahame's offer as insufficient.[10] This proposal having failed, a 21 year agreement was concluded with the GJ under which traffic carried by boats of the GJ carrying department along the GU was not to pay more than 6d (2½p) per ton for the whole length, except coal and coke, which were not to exceed 10¾d. The GJ tolls were similarly limited in favour of GU traffic. But even this could not be kept up: in 1849, the coal rate was lowered to 4½d per ton for all traders but the GJ. In 1852, unable to afford any further reduction, the GU got the assent of the rest of the Leicester line companies to allow returning coal boats to carry a back cargo of ironstone at a boatage charge of 2d per mile. It supported Grahame's plan to develop a trade in cattle and other livestock to the metropolis, but the necessity of persuading traders to build special two-decker boats for this trade made it little more than a pipe dream. In the middle 1850s, a complete reorganisation of the coal rates left the GU with no more than ¼d per ton per mile.

And so, with the dividend down to 9s (45p) in 1863, the period ends with the GU worrying as earnestly over its coal tolls as it had at the beginning. But there was now a difference—in those far-off years, the trade was there for the making; now it had gone, and the GU was to see even darker days.

THE LINE

The canal being safely opened, the committee gave its attention to its running and maintenance. It had always got on well with Bevan, whose handling of the GU's engineering was on the whole admirable (compare, for example, the shuffling way in which the LNU dealt with their tunnel crisis with Bevan's swift realignment of Crick tunnel when the faulty strata were found); and the committee duly recorded its 'highest sense of the attention and the great abilities' he had shown. Naturally, it wanted to keep him as engineer, but a man of Bevan's eminence obviously could not be expected to devote his whole time to a relatively small concern like the GU; so it engaged him virtually as a consulting engineer, to visit the canal regularly, report on it, and see that it was kept in good order, for 100 guineas (£105) per annum, a substantial sum for such a post. The arrangement was not a satisfactory one. It soon emerged that Bevan and the committee had different ideas about the time he should devote to the GU. On 14 August 1816, the committee inquired how soon he could give enough time to the GU's affairs, as it thought 'he should give many days continued attendance'. He had not replied by the next meeting, so they ordered that he should be written to expressing concern at 'his apparent want of proper attention' to the company. The following year, a bill for £600 arrived from Bevan, and, hinting broadly that it thought he was overcharging and it could only recognise £150 as the true figure, the committee offered him £350. But next month, Bevan came in person, and explained certain items which threw a different light on the bill, which the committee thereupon paid in full. Relations had obviously become strained, for the first time in the long connection between Bevan and the GU. Probably pressure of work was the explanation of Bevan's irregularities. Certainly it was not due to greed for money alone, for £78 17s 2d (£78.86) advanced by him personally to pay the landlords assenting to the new line for Crick tunnel remained unclaimed until after his death. After this brief period of uneasy relations, the old cordiality between Bevan and the committee returned, and he continued to advise and direct to the end of his life.

The engineer being present so infrequently, it was necessary to have a permanent deputy to act for him in the routine business. The committee therefore appointed Edward Buckley to the post of overseer. He was to live at Welford, in a house the company was to build, with two permanent labourers working under him, and was to inspect the reservoirs and feeders, regulate the flow of water from these, and keep the gauge of the water. His pay was £100 per annum plus the hire of a horse to help him get about the works. As sometimes happened with the GU, the choice was not a wholly happy one, and Buckley, on the few occasions he got into the records, was usually in trouble—failing to see that 'bumping pieces' were got for Foxton locks or to look after the fence at the toll house there properly; or that the engineer's orders had been carried out concerning a slip at one of the Foxton side ponds. In 1821, the subcommittee lost patience and asked Bevan to get a competent overseer in his place. Nevertheless, Buckley remained in his post until his death in 1831. Despite his transgressions, the subcommittee had evidently come to appreciate him, for it expressed a wish to give his job to his son 'on account of the long and faithful service of his Father', and 'Young Buckley' was given the job, but died only a year later—a tragedy to be repeated later in the company's history.

There were numerous items of tidying up to carry out after the opening of the canal. It had to be measured and the miles marked out, Bevan being ordered to use 'Derbyshire free stones' lying at Foxton, and to measure it from north to south. The fencing was giving trouble, the contractors, Wyke & Whitelock, proving unsatisfactory despite repeated warning. Even in 1817, the company was still complaining, but somebody remembered that Whitelock's solicitor was on the subcommittee, and it seems that the matter must have been settled privately, for no more is heard of it.

At either end, arrangements had to be made to connect the towpaths of the GU and the adjacent canals. A brick bridge was ordered at Norton Junction—the foundations had already been laid, but on learning from Bevan that this would cost at least £250, the committee told him to see Jessop of Butterley about a cast iron swing-bridge instead. At Foxton, a wooden horse-bridge had been erected, no doubt as a temporary measure while the two companies discussed the best method of linking their towpaths. One plan which was seriously considered was to extend the GU's towpath on the western bank of the LNU to the first bridge north of Foxton, about half a mile from the locks, rebuilding this as a roving bridge to take the GU's towpath across the canal. Nothing happened, however, until 1838, when the LNU built 'a very handsome and substantial Brick Bridge' to replace the wooden bridge near the foot of the locks, the GU contributing £125 14s 7d (£125.73) towards the cost (the LNU paid £136 5s 10d (£136.29) and the cost of upkeep was to be divided between the two companies).

But as already indicated, the chief problem of the GU was water supply. Sulby reservoir came into use with the completion of the Welford arm, probably in late 1814 or early 1815, although the contractors, Deacon & Mason, were not finally paid off until 1821.[11] As the second reservoir could not be made in its planned position, an effort was made to buy more land to enlarge Sulby, but it does not appear to have been successful; hence, no doubt, the committee's readiness to let Mrs Payne have land for her fishpond. Plans for the new Naseby reservoir were drawn up, and an estimate had been got for the feeder in January 1820. In the following spring, borings were taken on the proposed site. The work was entrusted to the contractors responsible for Sulby, Deacon & Mason, and the new reservoir came into use early in 1821. The position with regard to the water supply was thereby considerably improved, so much so that in 1822 the company felt able to agree to supply 500 locks of water to the Leicester Navigation in 'the dry season', although the Leicester company did not in the end take the water.

By the 1830s, however, the company was again looking for additional supplies. The work was done by a new engineer, for on 5 July 1833, the subcommittee read a letter from Bevan's son announcing the sudden death of his father 'that morning' (the letter is dated 3 July, although newspaper reports give the date of Bevan's death as 2 July), and asking for his job. This precipitancy must have been distasteful to the subcommittee, who, however, rather coldly gave him *pro tempore* the post for which his father had been preparing him by associating the young man (another Benjamin, like his father) with the routine inspections of the canal. Bevan junior soon began to find that he had insufficient time to spare for the GU, but he began the work of increasing the capacity of Naseby reservoir by raising the head, carrying out this work early in 1834. Two new feeders were brought into the reservoir, and further raising of the head was planned, the latter being ordered in 1836, when the company was planning a new reservoir as well.[12] This latter was duly made immediately below Sulby reservoir; it was constructed in 1837, Thomas Warren being the contractor, and was known as New Sulby or, more commonly, Welford reservoir.[13]

But before this, the committee had reaped the reward of its inadequate arrangements to supervise its distant canal. The post of overseer had gone to Joseph Gilbert, who, with no resident engineer to keep an eye on him, was to prove unequal to his responsibility, because, the subcommittee was later to opine, of 'his habits of placing his Judgement in contravention of that of his Elders in canal management'. The bombshell was exploded by the LNU, whose engineer, Francis Breedon, living at Saddington, was perfectly well aware of what was going on. On 31 May 1834, the horrified GU committee read a resolution passed at the LNU's General Assembly the previous month and sent on to the GU, expressing serious concern about lack of water on the GU, which, the LNU feared, might be due to poor repair on that canal.[14] The GU reacted swiftly. A deputation was appointed to visit the canal and report on it. The leader,

Page 125 Foxton inclined plane under construction: (*above*) the lower basin: Gordon Thomas surveys the progress of his design; (*below*) the engine house

Page 126 Foxton inclined plane: (*above*) lower approach arm and basins; (*below*) boats leaving tank at upper level

Henry Lawson, an experienced committeeman with a wide practical knowledge of canal matters, went down to examine the state of affairs, and, in what must surely have been a calculated slight to Bevan, invited Breedon, the LNU's engineer, to accompany and advise him. The invitation was accepted, with the inevitable result that Bevan's resignation was placed before the subcommittee on 9 June and promptly accepted without comment.[15] Breedon was appointed in his place, so that for the time both canals were under the same engineer. Lawson's report shows the canal to have been in a shocking state. Built to hold 5ft of water in the summit pound, it contained only 2ft, and the reservoirs were empty. It would be necessary to close it for at least three weeks for repairs, Breedon said, and Lawson philosophically commented that at least the water was so low that they were able to mark the position of normally invisible rat holes for future treatment. Leakage through the locks at the Foxton end and mismanagement of the water supplies there seem to have been the chief cause of the debacle, and Lawson roundly blamed 'the neglect and culpable inattention of the Officers and servants of the Company'. Oddly enough, he placed the chief blame on Lovell, the lock-keeper and carpenter at Foxton, and said nothing about Gilbert, one of whose duties specifically related to the control of water supply. Breedon, however, may have had his own views about this, for among the terms he proposed for his taking on the post of engineer, at a salary of £150 per annum plus travelling expenses, was a stipulation that the overseer should be directly responsible to him.

Breedon was an efficient engineer, and the canal was reopened on 5 August 1834, though not until late October were enough reserves collected in the reservoirs to allow rates to be lowered to coax more traffic on to the canal.[16] He had proposed dredging, and even deepening, the whole of the 20 miles of the summit pound, but little can have been done, for in 1836 he admitted that the canal was silted over much of its length, and proposed to dredge the whole in sections, using 200 men in gangs. In desperation to increase their water supply, the subcommittee had some streams diverted into the canal, to the consternation of local millers, and even tried to capitalise on a rival's misfortunes by getting the vast quantities of water being pumped out of Robert Stephenson's Kilsby tunnel on the London & Birmingham Railway, then under construction, diverted into the GU summit level (this proved impracticable, as it would have needed pumping). The opening of Welford reservoir seems to have settled the problem in normal conditions—in fact, after a few years, the company had more water than it wanted.

But by that time, it had lost Breedon, who died in June 1836, being succeeded by his son, another Francis. Young Breedon had come to the GU as surveyor when his father took up his appointment, but his tenure as engineer was tragically short, and must have recalled to many of the company's servants the fate of the Buckleys a few years earlier; for on 13 August 1836, two months after his appointment, Breedon was thrown from his gig, receiving spinal injuries from which he soon after died.[17]

This proved to be also the downfall of Gilbert. He was given charge of the company's works for the time being, and, soon after, his pay was increased from £80 to £110 per annum, with the promise of a further rise. But, having been given enough rope, he proceeded to hang himself. The GJ had allowed one of its engineers, Lake, to supervise the works at the new Welford reservoir, and Gilbert was ordered to carry out Lake's instructions. He apparently resented this, and was rash enough to utter anti-Lake sentiments which could be tied up with a bad slip of the bank at Welford. Gilbert had been treated leniently so far, but Lake was not the man to put up with this behaviour, and he took the matter before the committee. It snowballed, other people came forward with facts which did Gilbert no credit, and some dirty linen was washed in front of the committee, which duly found Gilbert at fault and—gave him another chance. Gilbert promised to mend his ways, but the effort proved too much, for on 20 July 1838, the long-suffering subcommittee dismissed him as having forfeited its confidence. It further decided to amalgamate the posts of overseer and surveyor, keeping Lake as engineer as far as his GJ duties allowed. Gilbert had the nerve to apply for the combined post, but the subcommittee passed him over, and appointed William Foxton of Ripon, surveyor to the River Ure Navigation Company. He was the brother of George Foxton of the LNU, and perhaps a relation of the William Foxton whose name appears as a shareholder of the GU as early as 1810. His salary was much less than Gilbert's had been, at £70 per annum plus £20 for fodder for his horse, with the use of the company's house at the junction of the Welford arm and the main line free. The damp situation of the house proving damaging to his health, he was permitted from 1845 to live in Welford, the company giving him £20 per annum in lieu of the house.

There followed a long period during which no major works were undertaken on the canal. The company had some trouble with the two railways which crossed it. At the bridge carrying the London & Birmingham over the canal near Watford, there were several accidents caused by horses taking fright at passing trains (as early opponents of railways said they would) and falling into the water, and a 'strong iron rail' was put up at joint GU and L & BR expense to prevent this, with success, it seems. The Rugby & Stamford Railway, a branch of the London & North Western, crossed the canal near the north end of Bosworth tunnel, and the horse path there had to be realigned.[18] At Foxton, bridges were put over the locks following a letter from the Leicester coroner, the result of a fatality in 1857. But most ominous for the future was a fall of brickwork at the north end of Crick tunnel in 1847.[19] It was followed by another in 1854.[20]

In this period, when for once the GU was free from major worries about water supply, and through traffic had been encouraged on to the line, it had time to try to build up a local traffic. There was never very much of this on the GU. The company claimed to have eight wharfs on the line, but only two of them, Kilworth and Crick, did any significant business at all, and for a time a private wharf at Welford did a fair trade. The company's wharfs at Kilworth and Crick were let in 1816 to John Foster senior and his son, another John, respectively. Foster senior's daughter, Charlotte, ran Kilworth during his last years, and took over when he died in 1831, but by the mid-1840s both wharfs had passed from the Foster family. There were inns at each, and apart from the coal trade, lime kilns were working there. Clay for bricks was dug (the pits thus made were a constant source of friction between the company and its tenants), but there was at this period no large-scale manufacture of them. In fact, trade at both wharfs was never extensive especially Kilworth, and at the end of this period the GU was seriously contemplating taking them back into its own hands and turning them into public wharfs. Another Foster, Joseph, had built up a trade in coal and lime at a private wharf at Welford, and the company established a landing stage of its own there in 1850. In 1856, the company itself became tenant of Welford wharf, probably in succession to Foster, for its landlord was Orton, the wharf owner.

THE CANAL IN THE 1840S

The GU was at its best in the 1840s, and it is fortunate that reports of the annual inspection by the subcommittee from 1844 to 1850 have been preserved in full. They present a picture of the canal and its servants as seen by a group of highly intelligent men in the course of a two-day inspection by boat (on one occasion, the delegation borrowed the Coventry Canal's inspection boat and toured the LNU as well, starting at Blaby). It was not just one-sided, either—staff members took the chance to ask for a rise or air grievances about their accommodation, Foxton requested a fortnight's 'holyday', and wharf tenants, lamenting their lack of trade, begged for rent reductions ('as usual' the subcommittee commented cynically about the Crick tenant). It examined the canal works thoroughly, and especially the reservoirs—'the water that they yield, being the Heart's Blood of your prosperity' as the delegates said strikingly in one report. Occasionally a note of mild exasperation creeps in, as in the case of the unfortunate lock carpenter at Foxton, who, after a year's sick leave, returned to work and promptly fell into a lock, laying himself up again. But on the whole, cordiality prevailed; the subcommittee noted with pleasure, for instance, that Atkins, badly lamed by an illness at the time of the 1848 inspection, was completely recovered on its next visit. The following year, finding that he had papered some rooms in his house at Foxton, it gave him 30s (£1.50) towards the cost, as being more permanent than the previous limewash; and his son, who acted as his assistant and did a lot of night work, was given a rise to 16s (80p) per week. The reports are racily written, quite unlike the stilted pomposity of the minutes, and the delegates obviously enjoyed their weekend in the fresh air, even when, as in 1850, they had to end their first day early and rush to the shelter of their overnight inn at Welford on account of the rain.

They were, in particular, inventive and knowledgeable about canal matters. Some inventions were those of the professionals, their servants—Foxton, for instance, experimented successfully with the use of hard bricks in the sides of bridge arches to prevent towropes cutting into the brickwork, a plan which proved to be cheaper and nearly as effective as the use of iron guards. The plan of sloping the canal banks down to water level was probably put to them by one of their engineers. But another idea devised to prevent the undercutting of the banks—by planting rushes to protect them—certainly arose from subcommittee discussions. It was tried out by planting stretches of 100yd with rushes, leaving the next 100yd unplanted, then another 100yd of rushes, and so on for 1,200yd, and the subcommittee was pleased to see that the idea seemed to work. An especially unusual device was the use of living mileposts. It was ordered that each mile interval should be marked by planting an elm tree at the correct spot, and each half-mile by a black poplar. The hedges were trimmed in a special manner to make these trees stand out even better, and the result, known, no doubt from its inventor, as the 'Lawson plan', pleased the delegates, who spoke of it as 'a very good, and novel, effect', as well they might. But the prize for the most bizarre scheme goes to Thomas Grahame, and probably arose during discussions as to whether the company should provide leggers at the tunnels, a matter which was brought up often, though nothing ever came of it. He suggested that, instead of the horses being walked over the paths on or near the top of Bosworth and Crick tunnels while the boats were legged through, special floating shelters should be made so that they could be towed through after the boat. What the leggers would have thought about having an extra load attached to their already considerable burden never emerged, for the scheme got no further.

THE COMPANY LEAVES LONDON

These delightful occasions tailed off, until in 1859, instead of the usual minute commissioning the survey, the General Assembly said that it would be much obliged if some of the subcommittee would inspect the canal that summer. The committee ordered an inspection in 1860, but no report survives, even if this were carried out. By this time, the company had realised that something drastic must be done if the canal were to survive, and in 1861 a special committee of six, which included W. M. and C. T. Praed and Thomas Grahame, was set up to consider ways of 'bringing about a greater union in the management of the Leicestershire line of Canals'.[21] With the hour came the man; and Grahame was the driving force behind the events of the next few years. He first appeared in the ranks of the GU in June 1847, when he was elected to the committee. His individual holding was only 5 shares, but he increased this until by 1860 he had 234 shares and 46 half shares. He continued to buy—GU shares were far from expensive—and in

June 1868, when he last chaired a General Assembly, he held no fewer than 454 shares. As the company's most substantial shareholder, he could do much as he liked, and the sub-committee therefore listened attentively when he told them in 1862 that the company could cut its officers pay—he said that they got two or three times the salaries of their fellows on the canals north and south of the GU and offered to produce figures to prove it—and save £400 to £500 per annum. He added that 'It is quite clear that we have suffered greatly in attempting to manage a Canal distant eighty miles from London in that City, and that Leicester should be the place of management'.[22] The decision to move the headquarters to Leicester was soon made, and on 3 November 1862, Cosier, learning of this, resigned the clerkship.

On 28 November 1862, Grahame and another member of the special committee, Thomas Christy, saw William Foxton and explained to him the necessity of making reductions in the cost of the operational side of the canal. Foxton offered to take a cut of £50 from his salary of £230 per annum, and was prepared to accept a further £50 reduction if he could have an assistant. Asked for his views on possible economies, he said that if the canal were his property, he would pay off a lock-keeper at each end, and cut the pay of the others; dismiss two of the eight labourers working on the canal, saving £1 7s (£1.35) per week; reduce the pay of the toll clerk at Foxton from £80 to £70, and replace his present assistant, who got 18s (90p) per week, with a boy at 8s to 10s (40p to 50p) per week; and introduce steam tugs on the summit pound. He added a surprising statement: 'Every boatman says that the Grand Union is the best Canal and in the best condition for passing Coal traffic of any in the line'. This seems unlikely, and does not accord with a curious incident in 1861. On 12 July in that year, the LNU committee had been shocked to receive a letter from the Traffic Manager of the GJ, informing the company that the GJ was contemplating working its traffic in the Leicester district by means of steamboats, but that when this had been tried 'some time back', the canal was found to be 'so much choked up with mud and weeds as almost to prevent the passage of the boats'. The committee, perturbed, wrote back asking in what parts the LNU was in such a state, and was no doubt greatly relieved to find that Fulton, the GJ officer who wrote, had sent the letter to the wrong person, and did not mean the LNU at all. Which canal he did mean is not said, but from indications in the address to which the letter was originally sent—the LNU's toll clerk at Leicester, whose name was Ruffell, which would have been far more familiar to the GJ man in its GU context—there can be little doubt that the GU was intended.

Whether because of the mental upset caused by this inquistion and the projected reform of the GU's organisation, which whatever its long-term effects on the canal, boded little good to the workers on it, is not known, but immediately after this, William Foxton collapsed and died while taking a snack in a Harborough inn, at the age of 52. The cause of death was set down as apoplexy.[23] To add to the confusion, Thomas Atkins, the toll-collector at Foxton, had recently died; he had been with the company since 1819, first at Watford, then at Foxton. This left the post conveniently vacant so that the pay cut could be made painlessly, but it meant that there were no senior officers to help the subcommittee carry through the reform plan, as Bentley had only been in office at Watford since 1856. William Foxton's brother, George, of the LNU, was asked to take over the surveyorship, while Atkins' son, William, temporarily acted as toll clerk at Foxton, where he was already assistant.

The economies worked out by Foxton and Grahame were introduced in May, the subcommittee encouragingly pointing out to its staff that they were still better paid than their fellows on adjacent canals, but the continuance of this happy state of affairs depended on improved dividends.

The company held its last General Assembly in London on 8 June 1863. It was a momentous occasion, when the new and the old met. Names which had been closely linked with the GU from the start are found in the list of the few who troubled to attend: Praed, Sale. But the direction the company was to take in the future appears in the new names: Harry James Davis of Leicester was appointed clerk, and the Leicestershire Banking Co became joint treasurers with Praed's. As with the LNU in 1809, the wheel had come full circle, and the GU was returning to the Shires, whence came its first conception.

CHAPTER 5

The Union Canals, 1863-94

THE UNIONS DRAW TOGETHER

ON 11 October 1877, the committee of the LNU considered an invitation from the Canal Association to join that body. It ordered the clerk to reply that it was willing to take out one subscription of £3 3s per annum (£3.15) to cover both the LNU and GU, 'and that it be explained to the Secretary of the Association that the two canals are under one management and are virtually one concern and state that as a reason for giving the two Companies the benefit of membership on payment of one subscription', which the Association duly did. The history of the two companies during the period under review is to a large extent a commentary on the truth of this statement.

In the direction, the movement towards closer co-operation began almost at once, for in 1864, the June General Assembly of the GU elected eight new members to its committee; all the new men had close links with the LNU, three of them being already committee members of the latter, and a fourth was the LNU's clerk. The rest of the old committee disappeared from the GU scene over the next few years, the last, J. R. Mills, MP, leaving in 1870. Changes on the GU committee henceforth were far more frequent than on the LNU—in this period, 93 different individuals served on the GU committee at one time or another, against 48 on the LNU. But 33 sat on the committees of both companies, so that for most of the period it is broadly true to say that, as the LNU's reply to the Canal Association implied, the two committees were in essence one body with two hats.

On the managerial side, the story is the same. Palmer, the LNU's clerk, retired in 1857 and was succeeded by Harry James Davis, who in 1863 became clerk of the GU as well, when the previous holder, Cosier, resigned expressly on the grounds that the company was transferring its administration to Leicester. Davis died in 1866, and both companies appointed in his place Hiram Abiff Owston, an eminent Leicester solicitor who held office as clerk to both companies for the rest of their independent existence. His was a difficult task, for the deteriorating financial position of his companies rendered expensive litigation undesirable, if not impossible, and they had some uncomfortable neighbours—notably the Corporation of Leicester, whose flood works schemes of the 1870s and 1880s were inseparably bound up with the interests of the LNU, which on occasion expressed itself strongly regarding the alleged threat from the town authorities. Owston's tact, coupled with the fact that the LNU usually managed to have representatives from its committee on the town council, enabled the company to emerge from its dealings with the Corporation on the whole satisfactorily. George Foxton, the LNU's surveyor, had taken over the surveyorship of the GU as well on the death of his brother in 1862, but relinquished the post in 1863, when Edward Hayes of Stoney Stratford was appointed engineer and surveyor. The vacant toll collectorship was filled by transferring Bentley from Watford to replace Atkins, the acting collector at Foxton (where Bentley was soon clamouring for a rise on account of the night work involved), and John Spencer, the new toll collector at Watford, was also detailed to act as assistant to the surveyor. This was regarded as a temporary measure, and one Pennock was appointed surveyor in 1865, Hayes being retained as consultant. Pennock was not satisfactory. He was unlucky enough to be in charge when serious trouble was experienced at both tunnels on the GU, and when 'serious deficiences' were found in his accounts in 1869, he was forced to resign. In the meantime, Foxton had resigned the surveyorship of the LNU, on 11 July 1867. The successful candidate for the post, of the 30 applicants, was John Parker, of the Midland Brewery, Loughborough. As a commentary on the financial position of the LNU, the company, when interviewing the six short-listed applicants, undertook to pay their second-class rail fare one way only! On Pennock's dismissal, the GU committee offered the post to Parker, who was allowed to accept by the LNU, his salary being reduced from £100 to £80 per annum, the GU also paying him £80 per annum.[1] The surveyorships of the two canals were thus united, and this was to continue for the rest of their independent history.

There is some mystery about Parker's subsequent career. At first he seems to have pleased both companies: in 1877, he was involved in a bad accident and seriously injured, and the LNU committee sent their sympathy and good wishes for his recovery. But on 16 February 1887, both committees ordered the clerk to give him three months' notice to leave their service and remove from their premises at Kilby Bridge, the Welford arm, and elsewhere.[2] No explanation is given. Parker asked for his job back, and got a curt refusal. The most likely reason is the deteriorating state of the canals, especially the GU, brought to a head by the trouble at Bosworth tunnel (see below). The two posts were advertised in the *Engineer* and *Builder*, and despite the impoverished state of the canals, attracted no fewer than 91 applicants. A subcommittee was set up, and after this had 'carefully perused' (so they said) all 91 applications, a short list of four candidates was drawn up. The successful contender, John Bourne of Penarth, was a disaster. After a few months, the committee demanded his resignation on 28 September 1887, and appointed instead Thomas Holt, who was to be paid £75 per annum by both companies, and to live at Kilby Bridge, in the LNU's house there, for which he was to pay £15 per annum rent.[3] Holt, who on 11 July 1892 was allowed to accept the surveyorship of the Leicester Navigation as well as his LNU and GU posts, was an unqualified success. Expenditure on upkeep had been cut so drastically that there was no chance of his restoring either of the Union canals to first-class condition, but the committees commented favourably on the all-round improvements they observed on their tours of inspection, and attributed them to him. When the companies were finally wound up as independent bodies, the last minute each committee recorded, on 12 November 1894, was a tribute to Holt, under whose management the canals had been 'materially improved', 'and considering the comparitively (*sic*) small amount at his disposal for repairs and maintenance, great credit is due to him for the successful result of his efforts to bring navigation into a proper working condition'.

TRAFFIC AND REVENUE

Trade, as reflected by tonnage returns, continued to fall throughout the period on both canals. A table of receipts at ten-yearly intervals shows clearly the extent of the decrease.

	LNU		*GU*	
Year	*Tonnage receipts* £	*Dividend*	*Tonnage receipts* £	*Dividend*
1863	2,017	15s (75p)	1,246 (half) year)	9s (45p)
1873	1,113	9s (45p)	1,127	5s (25p)
1883	838	9s (45p)	831	1s 3d (6p)
1893	735	8s 6d (42½p)	768	2s 3d (11p)

It will be observed that, although the traffic receipts of the two companies were approximately equal, the dividends they paid were very different, the LNU's being poor, but the GU's pathetic. The latter's dividends had in fact recovered a little since the year 1881, when nothing at all was paid. It managed 2s 3d (11p) in 1882, but fell after this to 1s (5p) in 1887, after which it paid 2s (10p) until the final full year in 1893, when, as we have seen, 2s 3d (11p) was paid. It is small wonder that the company's £100 shares could be bought for as little as £2.

There were several reasons for the disparity of the dividends. The first cost of the GU was far higher than that of the LNU, and the GU, with its two long tunnels, three reservoirs, and embankments, was much the more expensive to maintain; and, although expenditure was cut down below the safety point, it could not be neglected so much as the LNU seems to have been before Holt's appointment. But far more important is the fact that the LNU, as time went on, relied less on tonnages as the principal source of its income. This can be seen clearly if the total income, including tonnages, of the LNU is examined alongside tonnage returns alone. For the ten-year periods already cited, the figures are as follows:

Year	*Tonnages*	*Total Revenue*
	£	£
1863	2,017	2,832
1873	1,113	1,911
1883	838	2,009
1893	735	1,777

From these figures, it emerges that, whereas in 1863 the tonnages represented approximately 70 per cent of the total revenue of the canal, by 1893 this proportion had fallen to about 40 per cent. Other sources of income were being exploited, and the one which the committee pursued with greatest zeal was moneylending. It was prepared to lend sums of the company's money at fixed interest rates, the usual security being land or property in or near Leicester. The capital thus made available was the surplus of the company's income over expenditure, and, later, money derived from the sale of its property, and included a good deal which would more properly have been spent on improving the canal. The 1893–4 commission set up in connection with the working of the Railway and Canal Traffic Act (1888) pointed this out, but admitted that without this means of supplementing its income, the company would not have been able to pay dividends at all (at the time of the commission, the LNU had £16,000 laid out in this way). The first tentative ventures were made in 1864, when the assembly ordered the committee to sell part or all of the company's holding of £3,500 in Consols, and reinvest it as it thought best.[4]

The committee thereupon sold £2,000 of the stock, and put the proceeds in 'a very eligible Mortgage Security bearing interest at 5 per cent'. By 15 May 1865, the whole of the money from the sale of the Consols had been similarly invested, 5 per cent being the rate throughout. The committee seems to have been satisfied with these experiments, and ordered, in 1869, that its willingness to advance sums of money at £4 per cent on the security of land should be advertised in the Leicester papers. The immediate result of this was not encouraging, as the first security offered for a loan of £100, land at Great Glenn, failed to satisfy the company's requirements. As a consequence terms were extended to include houses as acceptable securities, which, in the developing state of the town of Leicester, gave the committee a far wider field of operations. But applications, of a suitable character, did not come in as fast as expected, and possibly as a short-term measure, £3,500 was lent to Leicester Corporation at £4¼ per cent. In 1872, the company sold the Swannington wharf at West Bridge, Leicester, to the Midland Railway, and the £5,000 thus raised was invested in the Leicester Gas Company at £4¼ per cent. A double purpose was served by a loan of £150 to its impoverished team-mate, the GU, for it brought the LNU interest and enabled the GU to carry out much-needed work on its line.

By the 1870s, the revenue from mortgage interest was beginning to form a respectable proportion of the company's income. The figures for the half-yearly receipts at this time are:

	£	s	d	
Half year ending April 1871	73	2	9	(£73.13½)
April 1872	146	9	3	(£146.46)
April 1873	192	19	11	(£192.99½)

At this time, it also invested, if that is the right word, some of its surplus money by buying up LNU shares, which stood at £6 10s (£6.50) per share. It did not hold them for long, however, and managed to unload some at £8 each in due course.

Connected with this method of raising additional revenue was the sale of a good deal of the company's property and the investment of the funds thus received. The sale of the Swannington wharf has been mentioned. Second only in importance was the disposal of most of the LNU's holding at Market Harborough. The company first thought of selling out here in 1873, when one of the committee members, A. W. Dalton, was instructed to survey their property at Harborough with a view to selling some of it. As a result, it was ordered to be sold by auction. Matters were delayed by a disastrous fire, which destroyed one of the LNU's warehouses on the wharf, Dalton estimating the damage at £798 (it was insured for £500), though in fact the rebuilding, no doubt at a reduced scale, cost little more than £300.[5] The sale of the Harborough property was then pushed ahead, the company probably having two likely purchasers in mind. E. K. Fisher and Henry Hopton, both with businesses centred on the wharf. Hopton, of the 'Bent-Timber, Steam Wheel, and Carriage Body Factory, London', ran an apparently thriving concern which leased part of the wharf in 1866, and wanted to expand. The first lot to be sold went to Fisher, but Hopton bought the Union Inn for £1,800. His firm was anxious to purchase the rest of the company's premises it occupied here, but after years of negotiation matters broke down over the price, in 1886.

Another source of income was the sale of water—not only as a regular feature to industrial premises alongside the canal at Leicester, Gallow Hill (where the Leicester to Market Harborough road crossed the LNU) and Harborough, but also, on occasion, to Leicester Corporation; thus, 1,119 locks of water were supplied to that body for flushing the river below Leicester in August and September, 1887, for which the town paid 5s (25p) per lock. The proceeds, £279 15s (£279.75), were divided between LNU and GU, much of the water having been drawn from the latter's reservoirs.

The sale of water was the GU's chief hope in propping up its falling income, and the GU committee dreamed up elaborate schemes which at least show that it had no hopes at all of increasing its traffic—had the plans come to fruition, the canal

Page 143 Foxton inclined plane: (*above*) the tanks in operation; (*below*) tank containing boats in lower basin, probably taken on the occasion of the Committee's visit on 11 July 1900

Page 144 (*above*) Watford: staircase of four locks; (*below*) Norton junction. The cottage in the background is the gauging house built in 1914. The view is from the GU towards the GJ

would have been incapable of providing water for a growth in the volume of trade.

At the beginning of this period, the GU was still troubled by occasional shortage of water: on 21 December 1864, the LNU complained that its traffic had been injured by boats having to 'wait turns' (ie if a boat arrived at a lock which was against it, it had to wait until a boat came the other way before it could pass through) at Foxton and Watford. Perhaps it was water shortage which caused the committee on 3 December in the same year to order that the canal should be closed on Sundays at Watford and Foxton.[6] But as trade declined, such complaints disappeared; the GU had all too much water for its traffic. By 1882, the position was such that the committee complained of the 'vast quantities' of water from the reservoirs being allowed to run to waste, on account of the 'slight demand' from boats. Finding that there were no plans of the reservoirs, it approached the General Assembly of 5 June 1882 for a vote of money to enable a survey to be made, in anticipation of calls from Midland towns for supplies of water for domestic and industrial purposes. The Assembly agreed, and Thomas & Taylor, of Westminster, were called in for the purpose. As a matter of fact, the committee had already been in touch with this firm, and had taken preliminary steps to clear the way for the diversion of Naseby reservoir from its function of feeding the canal to that of supplying outside bodies with water. A report on the feeders of this reservoir showed that two of the four of them were badly polluted, a third less so. The committee therefore wrote hopefully to Captain Ashby, the landowner whose farmyard was fouling one of the feeders, asking him to co-operate in ending this contamination as it proposed to supply water to towns in the Midlands; to the Bosworth Union Sanitary Authority, requesting an alteration of the drainage system of Naseby village, which at present was emptying into another feeder; and to the Little Bowden Highway Board, calling on it to put an end to the practice whereby local farmers washed their sheep in the third. It got a series of dusty answers. Captain

Ashby did not see why the Naseby ratepayers should help the GU to carry out a purpose not envisaged in its Act. The Clerk to the Bosworth Sanitary Authority also doubted whether the GU's Act permitted the proposed plan, but said that in any case, action lay against individuals, not the authority. His colleague on the Little Bowden Highway Board said that the sheep-washing matter was nothing to do with that body, and in any event, the practice was older than the canal. Nevertheless, the committee went ahead with the survey, and Thomas & Taylor duly reported that the reservoir had a 23,330-acre watershed and a 91 acre surface area, and held over 252,000,000gal—enough to give 67,334 people 25gal per day for 150 days.[7] Encouraged, the committee made approaches to two of the towns specifically mentioned by the survey as particularly well placed to be supplied from Naseby—Northampton and Leicester. Northampton was seriously interested, and asked for terms. The committee offered two alternatives—either a perpetual lease at £2,250 per annum for the first 62,000 head of population supplied, increasing by stages to a maximum of £4,000 according to the number of consumers; or an outright sale of the reservoir for £77,000.[8] But the committee overreached itself. The Northampton Water Company turned both offers down on the grounds that the reservoir was too small to justify so high a price.[9] Subsequently, Northampton made a reservoir of its own at Ravensthorpe, not far away. Leicester Corporation toyed with the idea of taking water from Naseby (and from Saddington, too), but eventually declined.[10] Thus the GU's hopes of selling water on a large scale came to nothing, and it had perforce to keep the reservoirs for their designed purpose of supplying the canal. But it is more than likely that the fact that the supplies were there was an important factor in the canal's future, for covetous eyes were being cast on the GU's water resources by a neighbour: the GJ.

TOLLS: THE QUARREL WITH THE GJ

There was far less juggling with the rates in this period than in the previous one, largely because rates were already so low that it was scarcely possible to vary them other than upwards, which would have been suicidal. But an acrimonious dispute broke out in 1865 between the GU and the GJ. As a result of an agreement made in 1847, it had become the practice to charge 6d (2½p) per ton on goods passing through the GU in GJ boats, whereas other traders paid 5½d, the compensating factor being that the GJ boats were not subject to a minimum toll, as the rest were, paying only for goods actually carried (the GJ took advantage of this by occasionally sending boats with as little as one ton, or even less, of cargo aboard). This continued until the GU severed its links with London, although Grahame, as chairman of the GJ, had pointed out the risk the GU were running in 1851. Perhaps the move caused or was caused by a breach in the good relations between the two companies which had been constant since the inception of the GU; there was certainly ill feeling on both sides, the GU referring bitterly to the GJ's 'considerable hostility' in this matter. However that may be, the GJ in 1865 demanded the repayment of ½d per ton on every cargo carried over the GU in GJ boats since the agreement was made. The blow was severe, especially as, when the GU subcommittee looked into the company's records, it found chaos reigning—more evidence of the weakness of the London-based organisation: 'Your Subcommittee have found that, for many years previous to the removal of the business from London, a very great laxity existed with reference to the mode in which the Accounts of the Toll Collectors were checked; and that a great variety of practice prevailed with reference to the charging of small cargoes of Merchandize and Sundries. The Minutes and Directions of the Committee were, in numberless instances, set at naught and neglected by the Toll Collectors, who appear to have adopted almost as many systems as there were Traders on the Canal'. Moreover, there was not a single officer on the staff who had been with the GU when the agreement was made, so that nobody could recall what was actually said at the time. In the circumstances, the GU was forced to compromise, and paid the GJ £200, in return for which the GJ withdrew the action it had commenced.[11]

THE LINE

Both companies had disastrous experiences during this period. The LNU's was the more spectacular, the GU's the more expensive.

In 1864, the LNU committee, mindful of 'the fearful loss of life and property occasioned by the bursting of the Sheffield Reservoir', set up a subcommittee to inspect Saddington reservoir to make quite sure that the same thing was not likely to happen in Leicestershire. The subcommittee visited the reservoir and feeder and found everything 'safe and satisfactory'. But the committee's presentiment, though misdirected, was well founded. On 22 and 23 August 1865, there was continuous and heavy rain. All the feeders became swollen, and the canal overflow weirs were unable to cope with the volume of water being carried into the channel. On 24 August, the canal overflowed on the embankment near Smeeton Westerby, water seeped beneath the earthwork, and the bank and towpath eventually collapsed, making a gap 60ft wide and 20ft deep in the side of the canal, which was drained from Foxton to Kibworth. Two empty boats, belonging to George Cooke of 'Box Moore', narrowly escaped following the water through the gap, with Mrs Cooke and three children aboard.[12] Foxton and his men worked hard at repair operations, and the clerk reported on 8 September that the canal was open again. The chairman subsequently said that it had been reopened 'within a fortnight', which would make the opening not later than 7 September.[13] For such a catastrophe, extraordinarily little damage was done—more, in fact, seems to have been done by sightseers who came to look at the spot. The LNU, on counsel's advice, was prepared to settle liberally to avoid litigation, on account of 'the known leanings of Juries against Public Companies', but the amount it had to pay in compensation totalled less than £140. The repair work cost a further £111 10s 3d (£111.51), being paid for from the Reserve Fund; overtime was heavy for some time after the disaster, and the company's not excessively paid workers must have benefited from it.

The GU was, as usual, not so lucky in its tribulations, and its reserves were seriously depleted. The first intimations of trouble came in 1867, when a portion of Crick tunnel fell while undergoing repair. This was reported to the committee, and on 31 May a subcommittee headed by Foxton was appointed to investigate and get the work of renovation carried out.[14] Traffic was evidently stopped, for the report submitted to the June General Assembly said that the committee hoped that trade on the canal would be resumed again as soon as possible. But soon after, a heavy fall of earth again held up work. 'A competent miner' was engaged, and, said the committee optimistically, 'there was a prospect of the works now progressing satisfactorily'. By early August, the company had paid out £358 for repairs, and a further £375 was outstanding next month, traders were demanding compensation (unsuccessfully), and some of the committee members were losing patience with their own staff. On 13 September 1867, three members of the committee drew up a requisition demanding that the company engage a competent canal engineer to examine not only the tunnels, but also the locks.

The committee gave way—it had no option—and turned for help to its powerful neighbour in the south. The GJ agreed to assist (it was, after all, in its own interest to get the GU back into shape as soon as possible), and its engineer, Hubert Thomas, attended a meeting of the GU committee to receive instructions on 24 October. He worked fast, his first report, on Crick and Foxton, being read by the committee on 30 October 1867. It was not a cheerful document. The east end of Crick tunnel was so dilapidated, he said, that 'I should not be surprised to hear of an accident occurring at any time similar to the one that took place a short time ago', and work should be started as soon as possible.[15] The committee, whose opinion of its own surveyor, Pennock, must have sunk very low, asked Thomas if he would undertake to direct the repair work; he was willing, but the GJ committee refused permission, and he had to decline to carry out the work, or to recommend any other engineer to take on such a delicate operation. Worse followed: Pennock, no doubt anxious to regain the committee's good opinion, went in search of fresh woes, and soon found another serious crack and bulging wall near the site of the first fall. He added, of course, that he was taking measures which he hoped would set matters right, but with the General Assembly imminent, the committee's cup of sorrows was running over, and it was in no mood to be consoled. The Assembly was gloomy, even for the GU. Profits were down, the half-year's figure of £504 comparing badly with that of the corresponding half year in 1866, £707. Expenses were up, and payments on repairs to Crick tunnel ate up whatever was available for a dividend, so that none was declared. The report was sombre. The Crick accident, it said, was 'of a far more serious nature' than had at first been realised, and caused the closure of the canal 'for some weeks'. The 'experienced Engineer' in his report showed that both Crick and Bosworth tunnels were in a 'far from satisfactory' state. Upwards of £1,500 had been spent on Crick so far, but still more must be laid out, as another defect had been found. At Bosworth, 'repairs are absolutely needed, and must be at once effected'.[16] Having thus faced its troubles squarely, the committee ordered the surveyor to get the work recommended by Thomas done, and advertised for a second boat to help in the repair work. By the end of the year, the committee members had recovered their equanimity sufficiently to discuss minor toll adjustments. Work was pressed ahead at the tunnels, to the detriment of the dividends, 3s (15p) being declared at each of the 1868 Assemblies. At the General Assembly on 2 November 1868, it was reported that work had been finished at both tunnels. The Crick tunnel account ultimately reached the figure of £2,484. The company had learned a lesson in one respect: it was recommended at this Assembly that at least £100 should be set aside annually towards the cost of the upkeep of the tunnels. In the meantime, it had to pay for the recent debacle. To this end, it parted with the holding of £5,000 LNWR debenture stock so carefully built up by past thrift: £2,000 went towards the Crick fund and to the agreed sum to be paid to the GJ with respect to the toll dispute, and the rest was invested, LNU style, in house property in Leicester (£2,000) and in Leicester Corporation (£1,000).[17]

Whether the work was done well may be doubted. Parker, in the early days of his career as surveyor to the GU, made a tour of inspection early in 1870, and found that, while Bosworth tunnel was in a reasonable state, parts of the brickwork at Crick had already been worn down to a depth of 4½in, and needed immediate attention. The canal itself was obviously in poor condition—the Welford arm was so choked with weed as to be unnavigable, and the winding holes were in such a state as to be unusable, boats to Crick having to make the first 7 or 8 miles of the return journey northward by being towed backwards, or to go on through Watford locks to turn. In 1873, the Weedon District Highway Board clamoured for the repair of the GU's bridges in the area, and threatened legal action, on account of their poor condition. Yet at the 1875 inspection, the committee professed to find the canal 'in a good state of repair'; probably a greater degree of shabbiness was being tolerated. Certainly when Parker reported in 1879, things had obviously got worse. At the time of his appointment, he said, the locks were in a bad state, but in the nine years since then, all that had happened was that two gates had been renewed, with a few paddles, though several gates had been repaired. In the last few months, two gates had fallen to pieces, the backs or 'hanging part' being 'perfectly rotten'. Some of the lock walls had bulged so badly that boats had to use pulleys to get through. The puddling on the embankments had sprung numerous leaks. Bosworth tunnel wanted repairing in two places, and at Crick, though in general the condition was good, the brickwork was 'shelling' in several places.[18]

The company does not seem to have done very much about all this—certainly no extra sums were allocated to increase the maintenance programme; on the contrary, the committee was far more concerned with cutting costs still further. In 1881, it stirred itself sufficiently to inquire about building a 'dredging machine', and sent a delegation to see one at work on the Oxford Canal. As 'the present apparatus is altogether insufficient', it arranged with the LNU to have one built at joint expense, the cost being estimated at £30 plus £45 for two boats, no doubt to carry the spoil away. For some reason, the building of these took an extraordinarily long time, despite the protests of exasperated traders, and not until October 1883 were orders given for the machine to begin work, manned by two GU and two LNU men. The company paid no less than £71 19s 5d (£71.97) as its share of the cost.

In 1886, the committee received an unpleasant shock. It was reported on 5 May that the brickwork of Bosworth tunnel, under the railway cutting, was showing signs of serious decay and needed urgent attention. With memories of the Crick fiasco, and perhaps visions of a train coming through the roof of the tunnel, the committee sent a telegram to Edwin Thomas, who had worked for them on the reservoirs and elsewhere, and who came down immediately to survey the tunnel. He found that the tunnel had been solidly, if roughly, built, being 4 courses of brick (18in) thick, but that many bricks had peeled off. However, he was reassuring: there were no signs of movement in the masonry, and he put down the scaling off as due to atmospheric influences. The remedy was to engage a bricklayer (preferably one used to this sort of work) to cut out the decayed bricks and replace them with new ones. The relieved committee ordered this to be done. With characteristic dilatoriness, the work had not been done or even apparently started late in 1887, and once more the committee ordered it to be carried out. As the energetic and efficient Thomas Holt had just taken over, there was no further delay, and he reported the work finished early in 1888.[19] And the tunnels troubled the committee no more, except once, when it received Edwin Thomas's bill for his 1886 inspection—in 1890. Perhaps the company's procrastination was infectious, but it astonished the committee members, and they minuted their surprise.

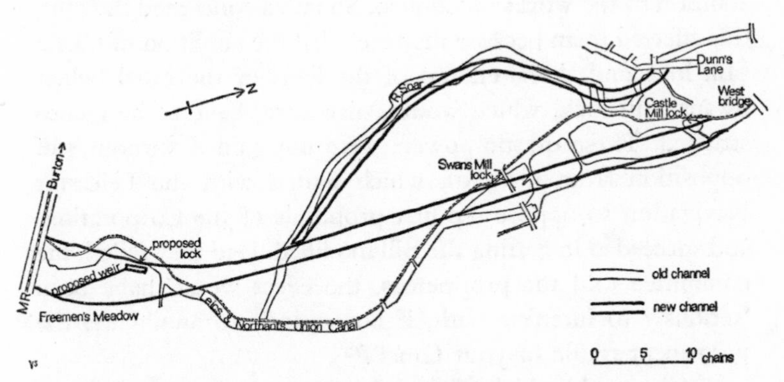

FIGURE 3. Map of Upper District of Leicester Flood Works, 1881

THE LEICESTER FLOOD WORKS

Leicester, lying as it did on the banks of a somewhat sluggish river, suffered badly from floods in early times, and in the nineteenth century the situation was made worse by the growth of the town, much of the land which had previously served to allow flood water to soak away being taken for building. It was said that at times nearly a fifth of the houses of the town were partially under water.[20] In the middle of the nineteenth century, J. S. Crossley and George Foxton, engineers of the Leicester Navigation and the LNU respectively, were called in to report on the condition of the Soar and suggest remedies for its tendency to flood, and their report was presented to the Local Board of Health on 8 December 1853.[21] Although it was reprinted in 1861 and 1867, little seems to have been done, until in 1868 the Corporation got an Act to carry out a series of works along the various watercourses through Leicester. But once more, not much happened, until in 1872, the Corporation bought Castle Mill, and in 1873 work began to the north of the town. As the powers granted by the Act to make the works expired in 1875, it was necessary to go back for a further Act allowing an extension of time, and the Corporation took advantage of this to ask at the same time for a considerable addition to the works sanctioned. So far as concerned the LNU, this affected them because they included the abolition of Castle Mill lock and the alteration of the level of the canal below Swans Mill lock, which would, of course, have to be reconstructed. These drastic powers were not gained without stiff opposition from the LNU, which united with the Leicester Navigation to oppose the first proposals of the Corporation, and succeeded in getting the Bill modified. Had they failed, the committee told the proprietors, the effect would have been 'seriously to interfere with, if not entirely to annihilate, the permanent traffic of your Canal'.[22]

But the works which affected the LNU were never carried out. The Corporation was fully occupied with the flood works in the lower part of the town, and before these were completed, an exceptionally severe flood caused a rethinking of the problem. This occurred on 12 and 13 July 1880, when two days of heavy thunderstorms caused the Soar to burst its banks, the whole of the upper valley being flooded. Leicester suffered badly, Braunstone Gate being 3ft deep in water. Frederick Griffiths, the flood works engineer, went to study the floods, and reported to the responsible committee of the town council, recommending a vast addition to the Flood Prevention Works Scheme in the Upper District.[23] The committee called in Thomas Hawksley to consider Griffiths' plan, which he duly approved, upon which it was sent forward to the town council, which adopted it.[24] The Corporation approached the LNU, which engaged Edwin Thomas to watch its interests in this major undertaking, and spent the next few months arguing with the flood works committee. At one stage, matters became so heated that Hawksley described the LNU's proposals as 'so preposterous, so unreasonable, and even so outrageous as to be beyond the sphere of discussion'.[25] Eventually, agreement was reached between them. The Act received the Royal Assent on 27 June 1881 (44 & 45 Vic, c 72). From the LNU's viewpoint, the major provisions were that a completely new cut was to be made from near the MR's Burton line viaduct, Freemen's Meadow, to the Castle weir, while the short stretch thence to West Bridge and the junction with the Leicester Navigation just beyond was to be deepened and widened. Both Castle Mill and Swans Mill locks would disappear together with the channel thus superseded, and a new lock was to replace them at the beginning of the new cut, near the viaduct; a stone weir was to be built alongside the lock, too. While the cut was being built, the contractors were to be allowed one week's stoppage of the canal a year, at a specified time, and they could have a further week immediately following this, on payment of £75. Other obstructions would cost them £10 per day. On completion of the new cut, the Corporation was to maintain it for one year (except the towing-path, which was to be their responsibility for three years), and it was then to be handed over to the LNU which was to maintain it thereafter. The lock, however, was permanently to be in the care of Leicester Corporation for purposes of upkeep, except for the gates. The Corporation was to give an equivalent amount of land for a new toll house at the new lock to that which they took in demolishing the old one at Swans Mill lock, and to pay £250 compensation for its removal. It was also to build two new wharfs to replace those destroyed—St Mary's and Mill Lane wharfs. If at any time in the future, water on the Leicester Pond became too low for traffic, the LNU could require the Corporation to build a side pond at the New Lock.

The scheme was modified somewhat for constructional purposes, the New Cut contract being extended from Freemen's Meadow to West Bridge, so that the contract to the north of it ran from West Bridge to the Soar Lane bridges, embracing parts of the LNU and the Leicester Navigation. This latter contract was let to S. W. Pilling of Manchester on 19 February 1883, and completed in 1886, having cost £41,600 against a contract price of £27,990. The Corporation had already had to get an Act to raise a further £60,000 in 1884, and, to reduce costs, sought to make a compromise with the landowners on the line which would enable it to dispense with the New Cut, and make the river navigable as a 'one-channel scheme'.[26] Meanwhile, the contract for the New Lock and weir at Freemen's Meadow had been let to James Evans, of Birmingham, for £17,883, to include 285yd of the new channel, on 24 February 1887. Negotiations for a 'one-channel' system having broken down, the Corporation decided to press on with the authorised scheme. Having, as a last resort, taken possession of part of the land required, they put the contractor in possession; he was Enoch Tempest, the contract price being £31,974.[27] Work went ahead with little interruption. The New Lock was completed in 1888, and the New Cut was brought into use in February 1890.[28] There were still difficulties ahead: parts of the bed had not yet been lowered sufficiently, and the LNU got £46 7s 6d (£46.37½) compensation for a stoppage due to the shallowness of the water from this cause in July 1890. The rebuilding of West Bridge inconvenienced canal traders, too. But on the whole, the committee was well pleased with the new lock and 1,635¼yd of fine, wide, straight cut they had been given, and told the proprietors that it was 'a decided improvement and that it has materially enhanced the value of the Canal property'.[29]

STAFF AND ORGANISATION, 1863–94

The tradition of long service continued on both canals. On the death of Robert Ruffell, toll collector in Leicester, in 1867, Joseph Nokes was appointed to succeed him, and stayed for the rest of the company's independent existence, although his own existence must have been in some jeopardy for much of the time—the Inspector of Nuisances sent a sample of the polluted drinking water at the Swans Mill toll house to the committee in 1883, demanding that a supply of pure water should be put in there; while when Nokes moved to the new toll house by the Freemen's Meadow lock, there was neither drainage nor sanitation. In 1890, two LNU lock-keepers, G. King and Amos Smith, both in their seventies and with about a century of service to the company between them, were kept on at reduced pay although no longer capable of a full day's work (though King, whose lock at Aylestone still bears his name, had to be retired on an annuity from a local charity next year; and Smith went at about the same time). On the GU, J. Harrold, after 49 years' service, was put on light duties in 1892.

Both companies made changes in their staffing on the grounds of economy. The LNU reduced the number of labourers on its strength from six to four, saving £80; and it cut the toll clerks' salaries, that of Nokes (Leicester) being reduced from £75 to £52, while Bentley at Foxton had a cut in the portion of his salary paid by the LNU from £30 to £20. As the committee said in 1882, 'The working expenses of the Canal have now been reduced to the lowest point consonant with the safety and the due preservation of the works thereof'.[30] Some would have said it had gone below that point: the London & Midland Counties Carrying Co complained the following month that the canal was in parts almost impassable.

The GU had been making staff cuts even earlier. In 1871, it paid off a lock-keeper at Watford, one at Foxton, and two labourers. It ordered that in future these locks should close at the same time as the LNU locks. It also considered the question of the toll clerks, and in 1872 dismissed Ruffell, the Watford toll clerk, intending to move Bentley from Foxton. This was not done, however, the Watford toll clerkship being ultimately taken on by John Bottrill. The committee was not happy about the Foxton post, nevertheless, and, in a review of possible economies carried out at the same time as the LNU's in 1881, it agreed to cut Bentley's salary from £80 to £40, but raised this to £50 on his appeal. As the LNU had also cut its share of his pay, the unfortunate man's salary was reduced from £110 to £70 per annum. In 1884, following Bentley's death, the Foxton toll clerkship was abolished, an arrangement being made by which Bottrill at Watford was responsible for all tonnages from traffic along the GU to Harborough and the LNU main line short of Leicester, while Nokes, the LNU's Leicester toll clerk, handled all tonnages on through traffic both ways and on southbound traffic terminating short of Watford locks. The toll clerk's house at Foxton was let to Mrs Bentley with a mile of fishing for £10 per annum. Nokes was to get an extra £20 per annum for his services, Bottrill nothing, so the company saved £30 a year, a saving which increased when, following the death of Bottrill by drowning in the second lock at Watford in 1889, his son was given the post, but at 17s (85p) per week, not his father's £50 per annum. As a final economy, the number of labourers, already reduced from 6 to 4 in 1861, was further decreased in 1885, another labourer being discharged.

THE SALE OF THE CANALS

It was to be expected that the ever-worsening position of the two canals would call forth suggestions for remedies. Not everybody went so far as a disgruntled shareholder of the LNU, C. Griffiths Smith, who wrote to the committee in 1883 calling for the canal to be closed completely. The Clerk was told to reply pointing out the difficulties in the way of doing so—implying that the committee had taken the suggestion seriously enough to consider it. A further letter came from the unconvinced Smith, but the committee took no further action, though with receipts falling every year, the ultimate probability of closure must have been plain.

It was quite obvious that neither the LNU nor the GU had the capital resources to bring their lines up to the standards envisaged by their originators, nor was their credit good enough to raise it by borrowing. Their chief hope of salvation was to be taken over by a concern with the substance to bring this about, and the only likely candidate was the GJ. As early as 1863, there had been discussion of a general amalgamation of canal interests between London and the Midlands, but nothing transpired.[31]

In 1887, approaches relative to the purchase of both canals were made by a syndicate through Thomas & Taylor. The committees, however, meeting on 11 March, refused to put a price on their canals without a valuation—to be paid for by the prospective purchasers. No more was heard of the proposal.

In 1891, the GJ began to show an interest in buying the two canals. A party from the GJ committee made a two-day tour of the Unions on 13 and 14 July, and its Clerk, Hubert Thomas, was instructed to write to Owston to try to find a means whereby traffic on them could be improved and increased. Whether negotiations were steered in this direction by Owston or whether Thomas followed a long-standing predilection as he hinted later, is not known, but on 19 August, Owston reported that he and Thomas had been discussing the possible sale or lease of the canals to the GJ. Negotiations followed in a rather desultory way, neither side being willing to name a price, until, on the Unions declining to 'name a low figure' as Thomas asked, he wrote offering £5,000 for the two. The Unions, no doubt not unexpectedly, rejected this as 'totally inadequate'.[32] In return, they named their figure: £25,000.[33] The two prices could not be reconciled, and the GJ then became so fully occupied with the Commission on the Railway & Canal Traffic Act that the matter was allowed to lapse.

It was revived in 1893, almost by accident, it seems. In an approach to the GJ for a toll reduction, Joshua Fellows, of the great canal carrying company of Fellows, Morton & Clayton, had said that 'unless some improvement is made in the Grand Union Canal their traffic would materially decrease' and had gone on to suggest that the GJ should buy and develop the navigations to Leicester. The GJ chairman, Stone-Wigg, told him that the company would listen to any proposal from him guaranteeing a definite amount of traffic if they did this.[34] Fellows immediately went to the Unions, told them the position, and asked for terms. He and Morton tentatively suggested £12,500, but the two companies had bigger ideas, and asked £20,000 (though minorities on the committees thought that £25,000 or £22,000 should be the price). On top of this, the GJ was to pay all costs, on both sides, incurred in connection with the sale, and mortgages and other invested capital were to be excluded from it.[35] The GJ turned this down flat, and was quite prepared to break off negotiations altogether, but Fellows persuaded the committee to let him have another try. He wrote to the Union committees pointing out that the GJ committee members were 'not anxious nor indeed willing purchasers', but only agreed to listen to any offers he could bring them to back him in his efforts to revive trade on the line; and he added that if trade continued to leave their canals (and he strongly implied that unless something were done, his own would), they would be 'great losers'. The committees climbed down, and agreed to let him offer their canals to the GJ at £10,500 for the GU, £8,000 for the LNU, adding, interestingly, that if the GJ wanted the GU alone, they would recommend this to the shareholders.[36] The GJ accepted the figure for the GU, but reduced that for the LNU to £6,500, and a further £250 was to be paid to Owston for loss of office.[37] There were wranglings over costs of the sale, and the GJ eventually offered £150 towards the £300 probate costs, refusing to pay more. The Unions were chiefly concerned to prevent the matter getting into the hands of the Official Liquidator, which would let them in for fees amounting to £1,900 between them. This being achieved, they were happy to let the matter continue, and at Special Assemblies on 16 November 1893, their proprietors duly voted in favour of the merger. It is touching to see recorded for the last time names coming from the earliest days of both companies: for the LNU, Hungerford and Isham, for the GU, Sale.

The Act met with little opposition, and received the Royal Assent on 20 July 1894 (57 and 58 Vic, c 85). It authorised the two canals (whose share capitals were recorded as: LNU £162,095; GU £278,600; neither had any debentures or mortgage debt) to be sold to the GJ for £6,500 for the LNU, and £10,500 for the GU. The GJ was authorised to improve or alter them, and to sell off lands, buildings and water as desired. Owston was to get £125 for the loss of each of his two clerkships. The GJ was empowered to raise up to £70,000 by issuing new shares or by mortgage for this purpose.

And so the names Leicestershire & Northamptonshire Union and Grand Union faded from the canal scene, and they bequeathed their burden of trouble and struggle to the great Grand Junction. Perhaps the kindest thing to say of the ailing little concerns is that their mighty successor did not make a much better job of running their affairs than they themselves had done.

CHAPTER 6

The Grand Junction Regime, 1894-1929

THE condition of the Union canals at the time of the GJ purchase is admirably summed up in the proceedings at the hearing of objections to the revised classification of rates submitted by canal companies in compliance with the Railway & Canal Traffic Act, 1888. It was said of the GU that there was a 'general objection of boat-owners to pass over the canal if they can avoid it, as in consequence of the silting up of the canal, the water is only from 3 feet to 3 feet 6 inches in depth, and boats using it are only able to pass along at a rate of about one mile per hour'.[1] The revenue for 1892 was £1,200, of which £678 was from tolls; the cost of maintenance, £994 (ie considerably more than the receipts from traffic). Of the 26,000 tons which passed along the canal in the year, over 20,000 tons was through traffic. On the LNU, the brick work of the tunnel and the locks, and the canal generally, were said to be in a bad state of repair. In 1892, traffic on the canal amounted to 37,000 tons, of which 23,000 tons went to London. As on the GU, the tolls did not cover the cost of upkeep. The coal, and even the Mountsorrel granite, trade had been lost almost entirely.

Why did the GJ buy these two canals, both apparently declining to their end? The motives of the sellers are clear enough. The report states that money must soon be spent on them or tolls reduced to attract traffic. The GU had no money, while if the LNU realised its assets to improve the line, it would have no dividends (Hubert Thomas once told the GU caustically that whether it paid a dividend in any year depended on whether it had managed to sell the hay crop from the canal's banks). The two canals were, indeed, trying to get minimum tolls of 5s (25p) authorised, to be imposed on boats passing the locks, the tunnels, or the 'Leicester pond' (the river from Aylestone to West Bridge), on maintenance grounds: legging was reported to have damaged the brickwork of the tunnels, and the cost of the upkeep of the new works at the Leicester end, which the LNU had allowed (wrongly, the GJ thought) to fall upon it, was expected to be high. The sale price gave proprietors of the LNU and GU only a few pounds per share, but relieved them of the possibility of heavy expenditure.

Fellows, Morton's motives, too, are reasonably obvious. They wanted a better line, capable of taking bigger boats—far more economical to work than the narrow boats which Watford and Foxton flights forced on the Leicester line—and only a takeover could produce this as regards the Unions. In 1883, Morton had told a Commons Select Committee that the answer to canals' problems was enlargement of their lines and amalgamation of companies, thereby reducing carrier's costs by enabling them to ship larger cargoes, and canal companies' costs by reducing managerial expenses. His ideas were being put into practice here.

The GJ's motives, however, are much less easy to understand. Perhaps Fellows, Morton convinced the GJ committee of the possibility of regaining trade on the Leicester line if enough money were spent on it—though a study of the traffic returns of the period before railway competition arose should have given rise to doubts as to whether there was now any prospect of winning enough trade to justify a sizeable outlay. Even a glance at the transport situation in the Midlands in the 1890s should have made the committee hesitate. Thomas said that one of the objects of the purchase was to attract some of the coal traffic back, yet the railways' hold on this in the region of the Nottinghamshire–Derbyshire coalfield was tightening—the Midland Railway, the sitting tenant, opened a relief main line from Nottingham to its existing main line near Kettering in 1880 largely for coal traffic, the Great Northern had spread into the area, the opening of the joint line through east Leicestershire by the LNWR and the GNR brought the LNWR into the coalfield, a position it began to exploit energetically, and the first moves by which the Manchester, Sheffield & Lincolnshire Railway was to extend to London as the Great Central Railway, serving the collieries of this area at the same time, had already been made. In this respect, the purchase was, in the classic phrase, a triumph of optimism over experience.

But men responsible for the direction of a major concern like the GJ do not normally act on hopes alone. Moreover, Hubert Thomas was no fool, and he told the 1893–4 Commission that he had been advising his committee to buy the Unions for nearly thirty years; probably this is related to his visit to the GU in connection with the Crick tunnel affair in 1867. 'There are very good water supplies and that is one thing that induced the Grand Junction to entertain the question of purchase' he said. He had no illusions about the Unions' profitability: 'What we are paying for we shall work at a very great loss' (he put this loss at about £600 per annum). About the poor condition of the GU, he commented 'We should not have bought it if it had been in order. We bought it for the water'. It seems, then, that the GJ acquired the Unions mainly for the GU's water supplies, intending no doubt, to spend money on gradually bringing them into good condition. At the knockdown price it paid, this was a not unreasonable policy, although it may be questioned whether a better one would not have been to have bought the GU only and endeavoured to close it north of the Welford arm junction, retaining the rest as a feeder to Braunston summit. But the GJ committee allowed itself to be carried beyond this, and to get involved in a gamble which did not succeed; and all lovers of waterways and the Grassy Shires will give thanks that it did so.

The GJ was also a little dilatory in deciding what to do with the Unions. De Salis produced a report on their 'present position and future prospects' on 19 May 1894, but by then the Bill had started on its journey through the Commons (it received its second reading on 11 June). The Select Committee agreed to go and inspect its prospective purchases in early August, a month after the Bill had received its third reading. And by the time the committee got round to discussing methods of clearing out the canals, the Royal Assent had been given. One thing it seems to have determined swiftly was its attitude to the Corporation of Leicester: it peremptorily ordered that body to stop taking water from the Soar for the Gas Works, but offered to make terms. Ultimately the Corporation agreed to pay £75 per annum.

The GJ also sought to continue its northward drive, and tried to buy the Leicester Navigation; but declined to pay the price asked, £38,150. Instead, it sought an agreement on through tolls, and this was concluded, becoming operational on 1 October 1895. Though the agreement was made to the satisfaction of the GJ and the Leicester, it did not please the Loughborough and Erewash, which were eventually included in a separate agreement running from 1 January 1896. Their participation was conditional on minimum payments of £200 and £100 per annum to the Loughborough and the Erewash respectively. This led to further talks, as a result of which the Loughborough was offered to the GJ at £25,000 and the Erewash at £20,000, the sale to take place within three years. More haggling revealed that the companies were holding back some of their assets, and the eventual prices, with the Loughborough still reserving one wharf, were £26,500 and £21,000 respectively. At these figures, the GJ subcommittee was prepared to recommend acceptance. The Select Committee thereupon agreed to extend the through toll agreement from 7 to 15 years, with the option of purchasing the three northern canals, the Leicester now being offered at £38,075. The subcommittee recommended the purchase of the canals, but the committee took no action, merely retaining the option of buying, with the expiry date of 1 January 1900.[2]

Meanwhile, work on restoring the line had been going on. Gordon Thomas, appointed engineer to the GJ on 13 June 1894, sent a report (dated 9 July 1894) on the question of mud in the Unions, with plans of a suitable dredger, which would cost £1,000; he was told to obtain one, with six iron boats at £110 each, if necessary. Work duly began, a 37 ton dredger being used on the 2½ miles from Norton Junction to Watford locks, from which it scooped 26,000 tons of mud at a cost of £500. A temporary road was then made alongside the locks, and the dredger hauled bodily up, with difficulty but without damage, and 18,500 tons dredged from the 1½ miles to Crick tunnel by 12 February 1896. The section immediately north of the tunnel was left for the moment while 2 miles near Yelvertoft were scoured, 24,191 tons of mud being removed therefrom, and then the Crick portion was completed. The mud was disposed of by paying landowners to permit tipping; the company had some difficulty in finding suitable places on some sections of the line, and was occasionally made to pay through the nose. By 30 June 1896, it had paid £11,159 for dredging, and £4,989 was transferred from capital raised under the Slough Canal Act, 1879, to the LNU and GU (Transfer) Capital Account. By the end of the year over half the GU had been dredged, and the GJ had spent more than the purchase price on it—£12,669.

Progress cannot be traced so readily henceforward, as interest had shifted from the restoration to the improvement of the Leicester line. It may, however, be followed as fresh sites for tipping were acquired. In mid-1898, the dredging gang could evidently get no land at Theddingworth and tipped the mud without getting the landowners' permission—for which the company had to pay £10 compensation and £3 3s (£3.15) to one landowner, £7 to another. On 13 October 1898, it was reported that land for tipping had been taken at Debdale; by 14 December, this was filled, and more ground at Foxton was taken. A new tip was opened at Smeeton Westerby in April 1899. By 22 November 1899, the line had been dredged to

Kibworth top lock, and a new tip was obtained at Great Glenn —at 'very excessive' terms, no other land being obtainable. By 10 October 1900, tipping had moved to the Kilby Bridge area, and in the following July, to Wigston Magna and Blaby. By March 1902, the dredging team was at Aylestone, having completed the canal section of the line. The date of the completion to Leicester is not recorded, but it was expected to be about the end of October 1902, the dredging gang being ordered to go on to dredge the Harborough section.[3] The Welford arm, however, silted from the lock to the wharf, was to be hand dredged.[4] The total cost of the dredging was some £21,650. In the earlier stages, expenditure had been fairly heavy—up to £4,000 per half year—but from 1898, it was severely cut, and with the solitary exception of the half year ending 30 June 1899, when it was £1,191, fell to between £454 (second half year of 1898) to £656 (first half year of 1900), presumably because of the heavy expenditure on the works undertaken at Foxton.

Fellows, Morton & Clayton soon made it clear that a mere restoration of the line was not what they sought. On 7 February 1896, they wrote asking the committee to consider enlarging the locks at Watford and Foxton so that they could use wide boats, thereby cutting their costs and enabling them to attract more traffic. A subcommittee of Stone-Wigg, Tatham, De Salis, and Praed was set up to investigate, which cautiously recommended that no improvements should be made before through toll agreements had been concluded with the northern canals of the line. When Fellows, Morton wrote again on 5 June 1897, asking what was being done, they were told this, and on a further complaint from the carrying firm that they could not use the wide boats specially built to pass the section, the committee agreed to go ahead with preparations to remove the Foxton and Watford bottlenecks, and at the same time carried the contest into Fellows, Morton's camp by asking what capital they were prepared to invest in improved craft for the line in its new guise.

But a new factor had entered. In December 1894, Thomas & Taylor sent to Gordon Thomas plans for an inclined plane (often at the time called a boat lift) based upon a design originally drawn up in 1886 for use on a canal in the Manchester area.[5] Evidence as to whose was the initiative in bringing this plan into the GJ's sphere is lacking, but Thomas is known from other context to have had a forward looking

N° 8504  A.D. 1896

Date of Application, 22nd Apr., 1896

Complete Specification Left, 22nd Jan., 1897—Accepted, 3rd Apr., 1897

PROVISIONAL SPECIFICATION.

Improved Means of Transferring Barges and other Vessels from One Level to Another.

We, BARNABAS JAMES THOMAS and JOSEPH JEX TAYLOR both of 1, Victoria Street, Westminster, Civil Engineers, and GORDON CALE THOMAS of Marsworth, in the County of Bucks, Civil Engineer, do hereby declare the nature of this invention to be as follows:—

This invention relates to lifts for transferring barges and other vessels from one level to another on canals and other waterways in lieu of an ordinary lock or flight of locks, the object of the invention being to obviate the loss of water from the higher to the lower level by lockage inseparable from the ordinary system and to provide for the passage of vessels simultaneously in both directions and at a single lift and between levels of widely different altitude whereby the loss of time incidental to the passage through a flight of locks is in great measure avoided.

The invention consists essentially of a system of lifts each formed by a wet dock wherein the vessel to be transported is waterborne, the dock being mounted on a wheeled carriage adapted to support the dock horizontally and to run on inclined railways extending between the higher and lower water levels, the ways being transverse to the length of the dock which travels broadside on so as to admit of a short length of wheel base and a steep grade. The dock is provided with end gates which may be opened and closed for admission and egress of the vessel by a rising and falling sliding or pivotal motion in a vertical plane or swung on hinges as ordinary lock gates, suitable grooves or chambers being provided for the gates to work in and suitable means of making a water-tight closure being provided. The end of the dock when at the upper part of its inclined railway makes a practically water-tight joint with the standing work at the extremity of what may be termed the head bay or pond of which the dock then forms a continuation, there being also a gate or gates at the end of the bay to retain the water when the dock is absent. The joint between the end of the dock and the standing work of the bay end is preferably a direct butt joint between suitable packed or faced surfaces at the leading following

FIGURE 4. Patent specification, barge lift, 1897

mind, ready to experiment with new methods, and it is fair to credit him with it. He must have worked on the scheme for the next year or so, and, presumably on his own responsibility, had a model made from the plans. In May 1896, Stone-Wigg, the chairman, reported to the committee that he had seen the model, at Bulbourne. He was impressed, and suggested that a larger model might be made, to which the committee agreed. The enlarged model was said by Gordon Thomas to be finished and working satisfactorily by 14 October, and the committee decided to approach the firm of Sir W. G. Armstrong to inspect it and give an estimate for a full-scale plane. Armstrong's, however, were not interested, so Thomas called in Hunter & English, mechanical engineers, who reported on 9 November 1896 that the plane was 'admirably adapted for its purpose, and will work satisfactorily with a small expenditure of power'. They were asked to estimate, and the engineer to prepare plans for the committee's inspection. Fellows, Morton were also shown the model, and gave their approval. In due course, Thomas produced estimates of the relative cost of wide locks and a plane, and in July the committee determined to buy land and have detailed specifications prepared for the building of a plane.[6] By 11 August, it had bought land adjoining Foxton locks, and on the strength of an assurance by Fellows, Morton that the firms would put extra narrow boats into service while the work was in progress, introducing boats capable of carrying 50 tons as soon as it was finished, Thomas was ordered to improve the main line between Norton Junction and London.

On 3 November 1897, tenders for the plane from three firms were examined. The lowest tender, that of Glover & Sons, Warwick, was £9,942, and the next, Hunter & English, Bow, was £12,390; but the contract when to the third and highest, that of J. & H. Gwynne, of Hammersmith, who quoted £14,130, 'as it included Hydraulic machinery for operating the whole of the gates in connection with the tanks and conduits, instead of hand power, provided in the other tenders'. None complied with all the specification requirements, and the contract as finally agreed probably contained features taken from both Glover's and Gwynne's tenders.[7] The committee also granted an additional sum of up to £500 for experiments sanctioned by their engineer.

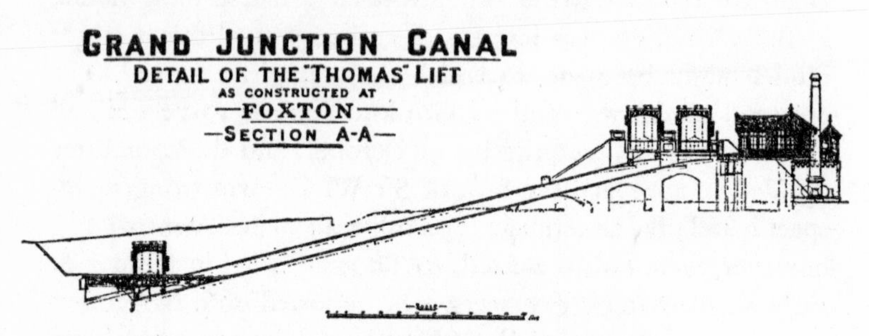

FIGURE 5. Foxton inclined plane: section

The plane was designed by Gordon Thomas in collaboration with his cousin, Barnabas James Thomas, who acted as resident engineer during its construction. It consisted of two enormous watertight steel tanks (moving docks, Thomas called them), each one capable of holding two 33 ton narrow boats or one 70 ton barge. The tanks were 80ft long by 15ft wide by 5ft deep, and were normally filled with water. When a boat entered, it displaced its own weight of water, so that the tanks were always of the same weight, so long as both were wholly out of the canal, irrespective of whether either had two, one, or no boats in. Each tank had 16 wheels in pairs, 4 pairs supporting each of the longer sides. These wheels ran on 4 pairs of steel rails, which were set in two great inclines or ramps side by side, the inclines connecting two specially constructed arms of the canal, one from the summit pound a short distance south of the locks, the other springing from the beginning of the Harborough branch at the foot of the hill. The tanks moved up and down the inclines, the vertical rise being 75ft 2in, with their greatest lengths parallel to the two arms of the canal, the wheel assemblies being pitched so that the tanks were carried horizontally at all positions of the incline. Wire ropes of 7in

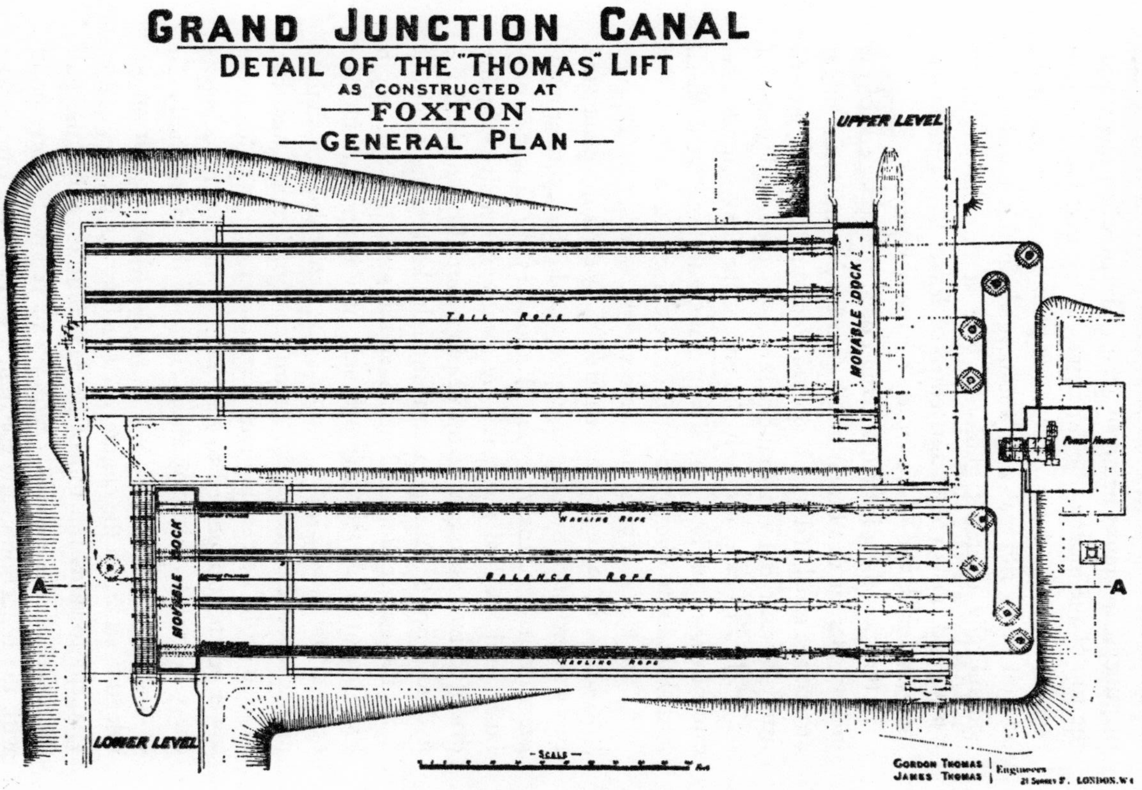

GRAND JUNCTION CANAL
DETAIL OF THE "THOMAS" LIFT
AS CONSTRUCTED AT
FOXTON
GENERAL PLAN

UPPER LEVEL
MOVABLE DOCK
TAIL ROPE
HAULING ROPE
BALANCE ROPE
HAULING ROPE
MOVABLE DOCK
A
A
LOWER LEVEL
SCALE
GORDON THOMAS
JAMES THOMAS
Engineers

FIGURE 6. Foxton inclined plane: plan

circumference connected the tanks by way of horizontal wheels or pulleys, the tanks being so arranged that when one was at the top of the incline, the other was at the bottom. The rails ran right into the water of the lower pound, and the tank at the bottom of its run was fully submerged. In this position, the hydraulically operated guillotine gate at one end could be raised, and boats could thus enter or leave. The gate would then be closed, and all was ready for the next trip.

In the meantime, its fellow would be at the upper end of the incline. Here it was brought up opposite the end of the upper arm of the canal, led to this spot in a conduit, and was pressed firmly against it by hydraulic buffers to prevent leakage of water. In this case, not only the end of the tank, but also the end of the canal, had a guillotine gate, and both were raised hydraulically to allow access to or exit from the tank.

As the tanks were of the same weight whether or not they held boats, little effort was required to operate the plane, and this was provided by a steam engine of a double-cylinder high-pressure jet-condensing type, of about 25hp. This not only raised and lowered the tanks, by means of massive winding drums driven through worm gearing, but also provided the hydraulic power through a horizontal duplex hydraulic pump.[8]

As the two inclines did not have the same point of origin (one began at the towing-path side of the upper reach, the other at the outside), the southern one descended at a slightly higher level than its fellow. A further complication was that, as soon as the descending tank began to enter the water at the lower reach, it appeared to lose weight, thereby reducing its effect in counterbalancing the weight of the rising tank. To overcome this difficulty, which would have thrown an intolerable strain on the engine, each incline was given an easier gradient towards the top of its run, thus lessening the pull exercised by the ascending tank on its fellow to correspond with the reduction in the apparent weight of the latter at the moment of immersing itself. As the lower tank lost more weight as it sank farther into the water until the loss reached its maximum at total immersion, the easing of the upper gradient took the form of a continuous curve of equilibrium, as Thomas called it, which he worked out taking into account the gradient of the incline, the weight and specific gravity of the tank and its contents, the friction, 'and all other of the varying circumstances of each particular case'. It also made the incline longer, since the lesser gradient naturally took a greater distance to raise the tank through a given height than the steeper slope of the lower part had. Furthermore, it was necessary to ensure that the tanks did not tilt from the horizontal when they came to the easier gradient. This was effected by providing extra pairs of wheels outside those of the upper side of the tanks. At the top of the incline, extra rails were laid outside the normal running rails from the point at which the gradient of the latter began to change, and these outer rails maintained the gradient of the main slope. When the front (upper) edge of the tank climbed to this point, the outer wheels engaged the outer rails, taking the weight of the tank, the inner wheels being lifted clear of their rails, which fell away at the easier slope. The tank continued to rise, until, at the moment when the rear wheels reached the easier slope, the outer wheels also reached an easing in the gradient of their own rails, conforming to that of the main rails, so that the whole tank changed its angle of climb and remained horizontal. The process was, of course, reversed on the downward journey.

Judged purely as a piece of mechanism, the inclined plane seems to have been effective enough, and in some ways looked well ahead; as in Thomas's arranging that the manual operations should be reduced to a minimum by installing hydraulic working for the gates (all of which could be worked simultaneously, as the pump delivered into an accumulator). Nor was it expensive to run, if Thomas's own figures are to be believed (and no others are available). After 6 months' working, he computed that it cost £1 4s 6d per day (£1.22½); in 1906, after 6 years of wear and tear, this figure had risen to £1 15s (£1.75). If it had been fully worked, it would, according to

Thomas, have cost 0·05d per ton moved; but this implied, in a working year of 300 days, each comprising one 12 hour shift, no less than 2½ million tons. Thomas or his committee, or both, were pleased enough with it to send photographs and plans to the Universal Exposition at St Louis, USA, in 1904, and were awarded a Gold Medal and a certificate.[9]

The obvious advantage of the plane in operation was the great saving of water, and this is no doubt why the plane was built at Foxton and not at Watford, since water lost through Watford locks fed Braunstone summit and the GJ main line. Whereas every pair of boats through the locks took two locks-full of water away from the summit pound, every tankful of water taken by the plane from the top pound was matched by either a whole or part of a tankful (when the ascending tank contained a boat) raised from the pound below, and the principal loss of water was by leakage only. In fact, when a descending boat was not matched by one ascending, and the rising tank was filled only with water, the summit pound gained water. The saving of time was of relatively small importance. An average run on the plane took 12 minutes (8, according to Thomas), against 80 minutes or so for a pair of boats passing through the locks. A saving of little more than an hour cannot have signified much on a journey between Derbyshire and London lasting several days. If trade had developed as the GJ hoped, however, it might have been a very different matter. Half a dozen pairs of boats at Foxton top lock, waiting to come down, and the same number waiting at the foot to ascend, could have caused confusion and taken all day to clear; the plane would have sent them on their way in an hour and a half.

The incline cost considerably more than had been estimated. Thomas told the 1906 commission that the total cost, including land, was £39,000, but the sums reported to the committee as having been spent on it each half year from 1897 to 1901 show that the figure was in fact £40,120. The constructional work done by the company cost something like £24,000 instead of the £12,000 estimated by Thomas.[10] This was probably the factor which decided the company not to build the one planned for Watford.

Moreover, the plane took longer to build than had been expected. Work was forward enough to allow De Salis, Praed, and the engineer to see a trial of it on 5 April 1900, but Thomas wanted alterations in consequence, and the actual opening to public traffic was thereby delayed. It seems to have been handed over by the contractors on 25 June, but the company recorded its official opening date as 10 July 1900. On the following day, the committee inspected it in the course of a two-day visit to the Leicester section.

In the meantime, however, a decision had been taken which involved the abandonment of the proposed plane at Watford, although not the widened line. On 5 February 1900, the subcommittee examined six schemes for alterations at Watford, and chose the widening of the locks there, at a cost of £17,000, and this was agreed by the Select Committee on 14 February. It was accepted that, if traffic increased greatly, water would have to be pumped up from the bottom of the locks, but the committee thought that the saving on first cost over all competitors (£7,206), and the low running cost (£50 per year) justified this. As the Foxton plane had not even had a trial, this decision can have had nothing to do with mechanical defect in the plane, and must have reflected the subcommittee's view on the cost of the plane (and even more, the cost of the associated works—shortly after, it opined that 'a firm hand' should be kept on expenditure here) and perhaps a well-founded cynicism as to the probability of trade growing sufficiently to justify the expense. Only two months later, on 11 April, it went a step further, and ordered that work at Watford was not to proceed until the Foxton plane was working satisfactorily.[11] The subcommittee's despondency becomes explicit in a letter sent to Fellows, Morton & Clayton: the GJ has spent a lot of money on improvements, it said, and 'so far, the results are not at all encouraging, the through trade, especially Coal, of which we had great hopes, has decreased considerably'.[12] It added that it was reluctant to make any further outlay until chances of a reasonable return were seen. Point is added to this, and the way its members' minds were moving shown, in a minute of 10 October 1900, ordering that, if Watford locks were not widened, the materials for the operation were to be used elsewhere. Soon after, the decision was taken to reverse the policy of almost a decade, and on 11 November 1901, work began on rebuilding Watford flight as narrow locks. The work was done by the Northern District maintenance gang with outside help, at one time 160 men being at work, and operations were at times carried on by night as well as by day. The side ponds, too, were renovated, being cleared of mud, the banks re-formed, the head walls rebuilt, and new waste weirs erected. The operation involved stopping traffic from 13 November 1902, with a further 3 days' closure from 4 to 7 February. The total cost was £5,545, of which £2,846 was for labour, exclusive of Bulbourne's charges for 3 new top gates, 4 pairs of new lower gates, 28 paddles for locks, and 6 paddles for the side ponds.[13]

As if to emphasise the abandonment of the company's hopes regarding attracting trade to the Leicester line, the committee on 12 March 1902 turned down offers of the Leicester, Loughborough, and Erewash companies to sell their undertakings to the GJ for £50,000. The Leicester was still intent on excluding some of its assets, the return would be only 3 per cent (even if the canals' revenues did not continue to decline as they were doing), and up to £28,000 would have to be spent on repairs. How unwilling the GJ had become to spend money on the Leicester line was shown next month, when it was ordered that expenditure was to be cut down to a maximum of £1,200 per annum, and no work was to be put in hand without the express approval of the committee.[14]

A factor which may have brought the company to disbelieve in the practicability of passing a great volume of traffic over the GU was the difficulty it had with water supplies on the canal. Leakage due to inadequate maintenance, coupled with legal requirements which restricted the GJ's use of many of the potential water supplies of the Leicester line, and perhaps the great evaporative surface presented by the GU's 20 mile summit pound, probably helped to bring about this unhappy and all too frequent state of affairs. One reason for carrying out the Watford rebuilding at the end of 1901 and early 1902 was that the canal was closed because of water shortage from the beginning of November 1901, the summit pound being 2ft 9in down, and no part of it was open until late January 1902. Several claims for compensation by traders had to be met. In November 1905, the summit, being 15in down, was first limited to boats with no more than 18 tons aboard, then closed. In 1907, half the bill due from Fellows, Morton & Clayton for night lock-keepers to pass their boats at night, a total of £70 4s (£70.20), was remitted, on account of the reduction in trade due to lack of water. In October 1909, a 20 ton limit was imposed on the Leicester line because the water level was down. This cost the GJ £48 6s (£48.30), which it had to pay to Fellows, Morton & Clayton for rerouting their boats to Nottingham via Fazeley and Fradley from August to October. Similar restrictions were enforced in 1911 and 1918, although by this time the committee had realised that total neglect was unwise, and as a result of protests from the engineer, had increased the annual maximum permitted expenditure to £2,050.[15]

The question of night working on the Leicester section ultimately settled the fate of the Foxton plane. This did not operate at night, an inconvenience to a north-bound boat arriving there in the evening which could have reached Leicester for a quick unloading early the next day had it not been for the enforced halt at Foxton. On 11 November 1908, the committee ordered that the locks should be restored at a cost of £1,000, so that boats could pass at night. This must have led to discussions as to whether it was worth keeping both locks and plane. There seems to have been no complaint about the plane on mechanical grounds. Thomas told the 1906 Commission that it was perfectly satisfactory, and described his plans for installing a number of other and bigger planes to improve the whole of the GJ system up to 80 ton barge standards (there would have been five on the Leicester section, replacing the seven locks at Watford and a further twenty-one to Wigston). Undoubtedly authentic stories are told of the rails, which were of inadequate section, breaking under the weight of the tanks, but only twice did the plane get itself noticed at committee level on mechanical grounds. On one occasion, it was ordered that spare wheels and axles should be got from Gwynne's. On the other, in 1909, the committee rebuked the engine operator for failing to see that enough glycerine antifreeze was put in the water used for hydraulic circulation, the result being that the hydraulic system froze and five cylinders used for raising and lowering the guillotine (the committee called them 'portcullis') gates were cracked. But, assuming that the figure given in 1906, £1 15s (£1.75) per day, for the cost of working the plane with its staff of three, was still applicable, it was not an economic proposition to keep this and add to it the cost of the upkeep of the locks. So, as part of a further drive to reduce costs, the sub-committee issued a resolution on 26 October 1910, ordering the closing of the plane after a fortnight's notice. It was used occasionally for a year or two after this, but in 1917 the engineer reported that deterioration was going on, and the committee, in view of the 'large outlay' necessary to restore it, notified the Southern Subcommittee of the Canal Control (this was, of course, during World War I, and transport was under strict government supervision) of its intention of pulling the plane down and selling the machinery. Permission to do so, however, was refused, 'pending further enquiries being made as regards any anticipated increase in Coal Traffic from Nottingham to London in the event of Foxton Lift being put into order, and another Lift or new Locks being built at Watford'.[16] Nothing further was done until 1921, when the committee again thought of disposing of the machinery, but decided to leave selling it until prices improved. In 1924, Blackwell & Son of Northampton offered £925 for it for breaking up, but this was refused. Again the matter lapsed until 1926, when the company once more revived the project of selling off whatever was left (later described as 'old boilers, steel tanks, steel conduits, hauling drums, wire ropes, etc.'). But it could not get the price it wanted—£250 for the engine complete, plus £175 each for the two Lancashire boilers. Not until 1928 were the remains finally disposed of, when Glaze & Whorton, of Wellington, Salop, gave £250 for the lot.[17]

In view of the collapse of trade on the Leicester line during World War I, the committee of 1917 must have had bitter feelings when it heard the starry-eyed sentiments of the Canal Control about 'any anticipated increase in the Coal Traffic'. The figures of traffic passing Foxton tell their own story. It should be borne in mind that, according to Gordon Thomas, the GJ originally hoped for 100,000 tons of Nottinghamshire coal to pass over the Leicester line annually. At no time was this figure remotely approached. In 1905, a total of 33,425 tons passed through Foxton lift.After a fall to 31,540 tons in 1908, there was a steep increase in trade, reaching a maximum of 41,520 tons in 1911. This no doubt reflects the fact that it was now possible to pass Foxton at night by way of the locks. In 1910, the subcommittee had determined to close King's (Aylestone), Newton Harcourt, and Foxton locks between 8pm and 5am from April to September, and from 6pm to 6am for the rest of the year, but had deferred this pending discussions with Fellows, Morton & Clayton, and night operation was still in force at least as late as 24 April 1911. On that day, the subcommittee suggested that steamers should be allowed to pass at night between Kibworth and Aylestone if accompanied by one of the company's servants, Fellows, Morton & Clayton paying half the cost. No reply is recorded from the carriers, but it is significant that traffic figures fell henceforth until in 1914 they were down to 34,910 tons. After this, the collapse was dramatic. World War I, which elsewhere was creating problems by increasing the volume of traffic immensely, had the effect on the Leicester line of cutting through traffic by two-thirds: in 1918, only 10,386 tons passed through

Foxton. The postwar years saw a continuation of the downward trend, despite occasional years in which an increase was shown: 1925 was an exceptional year, with 12,514 tons through the locks. In 1929, the return had fallen to a pathetic 7,216 tons. Only in March of that year did the tonnage reach four figures. For most of the year, boating on the Leicester line must have been a lonely experience.

In view of the restrictions the committee put on expenditure, it is surprising how much work the engineer managed to get done on the line. In April 1911, bridge 69 in Smeeton Westerby parish was ordered to be rebuilt, as being in need of 'very extensive repairs'.[18] The extent to which the Leicester line had fallen out of favour may be seen by comparing bridge No 66, built in 1898 in the rather unattractively opulent style adopted for the bridle road bridge over the lower arm to Foxton lift, with the rebuilt No 69; the latter solid, untilitarian and plain, though it carries a public road, while the much more pretentious No 66 bears only a cart road, whose purpose, to connect Debdale wharf with the village of Smeeton Westerby, can have had little significance by 1898. In the same year, locks 22 and 23 at Aylestone were thoroughly repaired at a cost of £950, so quite a high proportion of the revenue from the line in this, its most successful year under GJ management, must have been ploughed back. An effort was made to remedy a defect which had long been complained about by Langham, the local landowner concerned: the leakage from the pounds between locks 10 and 12 (Wigston Magna) by which 3,500 locks of water were lost annually. Thomas drew up a plan for a deep wall 300yd long, at a cost of £1,350, and this was adopted. But on 28 February 1916, before the scheme was carried out, Gordon Thomas was dismissed from the company's service, and his successor as engineer, Yates, reported that the wall, of which 47ft had been built, was not likely to succeed. The committee thereupon agreed to adopt instead his idea of a concrete invert with concrete sidewalls, to cost £5 5s per yard. The work was completed during a stoppage at the end of November. The fact that the committee was prepared to tolerate for years a regular and considerable loss of water in this way rather than increase the allowance for maintenance in order to end it, no doubt indicates their lack of enthusiasm for the line.

Considering that traffic was falling rapidly, and that the nation's manpower had other things to occupy it, the company got an extraordinary amount of maintenance done during World War I. In 1917, it had to build the bridge over the quiet little road between Smeeton Westerby and Saddington anew owing to its dangerous condition. While this was being done (it lasted until March 1918 owing to trouble with the foundations in the rebuilding), it was found that urgent repairs were needed to Saddington tunnel nearby, and the southern approaches to it had to be cleaned out. The committee, with commendable opportunism, decreed that the work should be done immediately the bridge rebuilding was finished, using the men from the Transport Workers Battalion who were employed on that job. It also got a grant from the Market Harborough Rural District Council for widening the bridge from 13ft to 16ft; the total cost was £1,123, of which the RDC paid £50, while the tunnel and approach work cost £800. The year 1918 was thus expensive and unremunerative, as was 1919, since Smeeton aqueduct had to be repaired, the estimated cost being £1,500.

Links with the independent Union Canals were gradually broken. Nokes, the Leicester toll clerk, was pensioned off at £1 per week in 1902. His successor, W. J. Cherry, was brought from Brentford and occupied the Leicester toll office alongside the New Lock until, on 23 December 1921, the committee, having looked into the state of affairs at the Leicester end, and found that there 'very little work to perform there', closed the office down and pensioned Cherry off. Through tolls were now taken at Norton Junction only.

In 1914, the GJ lost a valuable servant when Thomas Holt resigned through old age. As he had been the surveyor of both Unions and of the Leicester Navigation—and had nearly been clerk of works to the Leicester Flood Prevention Works scheme, his appointment having been overthrown by an amendment at the Flood Works Committee meeting dealing with the matter—the GJ was wise to retain him, and he was rewarded by the generous pension of £130 per annum. His successor, H. J. Walker, overseer of the Middle District, was to be paid £160 per annum, and to be provided with a motor cycle. (In 1918, T. W. Millner, Assistant Engineer on the Northern and Leicester section, was bought a motor car, though only a second-hand one; and a few weeks later, to counteract this concession to the mechanical age, the company bought a horse for use on the Leicester section.)

But as the 1920s ran their course, the sands were running out for the GJ. In 1929, it became part of the great canal amalgamation which revived the old name of Grand Union, as literally descriptive of it as of the original. Thus, after only 35 years, the Union canals changed hands again; but their poor record under GJ management made it fairly sure that, whatever ambitions the great new company had, the Leicester line would come low in the list of priorities.

CHAPTER 7

Trends, 1929-71

FROM 1 January 1929, the former Union canals were a part of the new Grand Union Canal system. The idea of a unified canal line linking London and the Midlands, dreamed of by men like Thomas Grahame, had at last very nearly been realised, though as events were to show, too late.

The new company had no intention of sitting back hoping that canal affairs would improve of themselves. It put in hand an ambitious scheme of development, but concentrated, rightly, on the Birmingham line, leaving the Leicester line Cinderella for a future time. That time came in 1931, when work was in full swing on the main line. As a preliminary to putting the whole of the Leicester line into shape, the GU bought the Leicester, Loughborough, and Erewash canals for £75,000; an action which may have reminded those with long memories of the GJ's purchase of the Unions in 1894—an inauspicious precedent.

The next step—although in fact, the preparatory work went on more or less simultaneously with the purchase of the northern canals of the line, purchase and works being authorised by the same Act, the Grand Union Canal (Leicester Canals Purchase etc) Act, 21 & 22 Geo V, c 107, of 31 July 1931—was to remove the bottlenecks at Foxton and Watford. There was no talk of lifts this time. The locks were to be replaced by wide locks—not a rebuilding, for the line to be followed differed from the existing one at each place. At Foxton, the 10 narrow locks were to be replaced by 8 wide ones, raising the canal 73ft 7in; at Watford, 6 wide locks were to take the place of the 7 narrow, the fall being 54ft 8in. The new flight at Foxton was to be to the west of the existing one. The new line at Watford, on the other hand, was east of the old GU one, and would follow the line chosen by Gordon Thomas for the lift he proposed as part of his great scheme for upgrading the GJ system to big boat standards. The middle pair of locks here were to form a riser. The Foxton flight was apparently intended to be a staircase, unlike those which it was to replace, which took the form of two staircases of 5 locks each with a passing place between them. Whether this could or would have been altered in the building (the Act would have allowed this, within limits), we shall never know; for events did not fall out as the GU had planned. In 1929, the government, willing to support measures to create work at a time when unemployment figures were high, though not yet racing upwards with horrifying speed as they were soon to do, was ready to make financial grants to encourage schemes such as the GU's improvements on the Braunston to Birmingham line. By 1931, however, the political scene had changed, and when the GU approached the government for financial aid towards the £144,000 needed to carry out the Foxton and Watford widening, it was refused. The company was thus faced with the fact that, if it went ahead with the scheme, by the time it had finished it would have spent nearly 2¼ million pounds on a line which had shown no signs of improving its trade for many years. The GU very sensibly heeded the awful warning of the GJ's debacle at the turn of the century, and dropped the scheme.[1]

In effect, this marks the end of any hope of making the Leicester line commercially profitable. Traffic continued along it, of course, but, despite the heroic efforts of the company in creating the Grand Union Canal Carrying Company, decline continued until by the outbreak of World War II, there was very little trade. War had its usual effect of upsetting the natural traffic pattern, and there was an increase of trade on the line, though this was somewhat intermittent and seldom more than slight (one's wartime recollections of the Unions are of a stretch of tranquil beauty in a maniac world, with rarely a boat to be seen). With the return of peace, traffic again dwindled.

By great good fortune, two classic accounts of the line by observant and sensitive writers, were compiled at about this time. The first is contained in L. T. C. Rolt's *Narrow Boat*, describing his travels in the narrow boat *Cressy* over our waterways in 1939. He spent three days on the Unions—the 'lost and lovely waterway' as he aptly calls the GU—and during that time he met no other boat. Crick wharf was disused, as was that near Yelvertoft. He was more fortunate than the present day traveller at North Kilworth, for, while there was little trade there, the inn, the 'Union Anchor' was still open and quite unspoiled. On the Old Union, the Harborough branch was so choked with weed as to interfere seriously with the cooling system of his engine. He says little of the line between Foxton and Leicester, which he evidently did not like very much![2]

The second, by Susan Woolfitt, in her delightful book *Idle Women*, an account of her experiences as a wartime boatwoman with the GUCC CO, is written from the point of view of the working boater.[3] The state in which she found the GU summit pound from Watford to Foxton shows how little use it had (as did the fact that she welcomed the chance of making the trip as a rare event). She and her comrade (they were working a pair of empty boats north) found that the line was a narrow channel of open water in the middle of a mass of weed; if they deviated from this channel, their propeller was fouled at once. Although their boats were empty, it took them 6½ hours to cover the 20 mile top pound. On the return journey, with 46 tons of coal from Langley Mill, they took 10 hours. They found the Old Union better, but its reputation among boaters was obviously bad.

By the middle 1950s, trade had practically left the Leicester line. The southern section was not mentioned specifically in the Report of the Board of Survey on Canals and Waterways, published in 1955, but by implication the Board had not much hope for its future commercially: its comment that narrow canals capable of carrying 50 tons per pair of boats were particularly vulnerable to the competition of road vehicles working under 'C' licences, especially where the locks were narrow, applies of course to the Unions.[4] However, the line was included in the list of canals recommended for retention but not development.[5]

In 1963, an effort was made to revive trade, the firm of Seymour Roseblade being first in the field. The first boats to pass through Foxton locks, the narrow boat *Neptune* and butty *Cedar*, on the new venture, did so on 17 May 1964, when they were said to be the first working boats to pass the locks for eight years.[6] The first traffic was wisely selected—timber from Wisbech to Leicester—for the road system between Leicester and the eastern counties is very poor. North-south traffic has much less chance of success, with the steady progress of the construction of the M1 linking London and the north through the heart of the East Midlands, although there was some timber traffic between Brentford and Leicester. Nevertheless, the attempted revival was not successful, and yet again commercial traffic declined to the occasional boat.

The interim report issued by the British Waterways Board in 1964, *The Future of the Waterways*, was not encouraging as regards the Unions. The old GU, it is true, figured as important for water supply.[7] As regards pleasure cruising, however, as well as other purposes, the Unions only got a mention as 'other possibilities', with the comment that the Norton to Leicester section was not extensively used for pleasure cruising, and that careful thought would have to be given to the question of their retention for this purpose.[8] In the following year, the Board reiterated, in *The Facts about the Waterways*, that there was no extensive use of the line by pleasure craft, and pointed out that expenditure in 1964 heavily outweighed receipts—a mere £6,499 income (of which £3,141 came from the sale of water), against an expenditure of £50,571 (of which maintenance cost £41,641). The deficit was £3,776 greater than in 1963.[9] The outlook was not bright for the Unions.

THE GROWTH OF PLEASURE TRAFFIC

But interest in the line among the boating fraternity, and among the increasing number of those seeking the last strongholds of peace and quiet in an increasingly noisy and restless age, was growing, and even while the public were reading the Board's somewhat depressing findings, things were happening which were to help put the line on the pleasure cruising map.

Pleasure traffic had not been envisaged as a source of income for either canal at their inception, and no rate of toll was laid down for this purpose. The LNU Act of 1793 included a clause allowing landowners on the line to put their own pleasure boats on the canal free of toll, provided that they did not pass through a lock when water was not running to waste over the weir; if they did, they were to be charged as for 10 tons. On the GU line, Mrs Bennett of Watford was granted the same privilege as part of the deal by which she agreed to the company's deviation of its line through her park. There is no evidence that much use was made of these concessions. One Bunney was forced to make a public apology for passing through a lock in his pleasure boat and so wasting water in 1797, and a young man was nearly brained by a stone dropped on him from West Bridge while he was rowing in 1831, otherwise it does not seem that either canal was used by authorised pleasure boats for many years.[10] How much surreptitious joy-riding was done, especially on the GU's 20 mile pound, is unknown, but that it was possible to get away with a certain amount of free-trading is shown as late as 1889, when the committee members, on an inspection, took it into their heads to inquire into the credentials of two boat-houses at Husbands Bosworth and one at Lubenham Lodge, and found that none of them had the company's sanction, though all lay wholly or partly on company's land. Their owners were ordered to be charged 10s (50p) for the boathouse and use of a boat. Other GU records mainly concern Welford reservoir: at first 10s (50p) per annum was charged for the privilege of keeping a boat on it, and in at least one case, this included permission to fish. But by 1888, the GU had a better appreciation of its assets, and in that year charged Mr Kitchen, of the George Inn, Welford, £5 per annum to cover permission to keep a boat on the reservoir and to fish.

The earliest recorded mention of a pleasure boat on the GU occurs in 1884, when H. E. Hamshaw got permission to use his canoe on both GU and LNU for 10s 6d (52½p) each canal. On the LNU, apart from the cases quoted above, pleasure traffic is noted earlier, for in 1863 W. C. Morley of the Temple was asked to pay 10s (50p) to pass over the canal in his pleasure boat in the Whitsun holidays. By 1869, there was at least enough interest in boating on the LNU for the committee to lay down a fixed charge for pleasure boats: 1 guinea (£1.05) per annum, but if they were horse towed, they were to pay as for 20 tons. In 1870, they sent their surveyor round to find out if any boats had been thus horse drawn, and he caught Mr Douglass of Market Harborough, who had not only used a pony to pull his boat once, but seems to have been £3 3s (£3.15) in arrears with his licence fees. The company sent him a bill, demanding 6s 8d (34p) for the one horse-drawn trip, but relinquished the claim on his protesting, though they insisted that he must in future pay £1 1s (£1.05) for boat and boathouse.

An interesting special case was that of Montague Brown, curator of Leicester Museum, who was allowed to put his canoe on the canal free (though he was to carry it round locks) in order to collect 'plants, Beetles, and other objects of natural History for study and to add to the Museum Collection'.

Most of these were probably small craft, but a hint of larger vessels comes in 1888, when Mr Smedley of Wigston was allowed to put a steam launch on the canal, being given the option of paying £15 per annum or tonnage of 13s 4d (66½p) per journey.

Soon after this, the ancestors of the modern firms who provide boats for the pleasure of others appeared, when in 1890, two men named Gulson and Jobson put pleasure steamers on

Leicester pound. The committee wanted £10 per annum each, but Jobson protested that this was too much for little steamers, and the toll was reduced to £5 each.

At Aylestone, a thriving trade arose in hiring rowing boats, the owner arranging with the company that he should fix rollers on the banks of the canal at the locks so that boats could pass round the latter. Parts of the river were incorporated in the route, the enterprising Mr Biggs, owner of the boathouse, christening the backwaters of the Soar with romantic and highly inappropriate names, drawn from such sources as Longfellow—Hiawatha, Nokomis, and the like. But perhaps the most surprising thing that happened in the uncommercial line was a lifeboat demonstration in 1894, at Leicester, of all towns most remote from the sea.

This, then, was the background against which a number of people sought to give the Union canals a new lease of life as waterways for pleasure. The significant date was 1964. In that year, the British Waterways Board undertook a study which showed that, should future traffic justify it, concrete ramps and tractor-drawn cradles could be installed at Foxton and Watford to enable broad cruisers to pass from the Thames to the Trent. In 1964, too, a firm started business building most excellent boats both for sale and for hire at the canal basin, Market Harborough. It has enjoyed a deserved success, and other hire firms have since opened at North Kilworth and Crick. The same year also saw the foundation of the Old Union Canal Society, a body of lovers of the Leicester line, some with boats, others without, whose aim is to study the waterway from Norton Junction northwards in all its aspects, and to do all in their power to help in the revival of traffic. They played a notable part in helping British Waterways in the restoration of the Welford arm in 1968–9. Much credit is due also to British Waterways, who with much to do and all too little money and staff to do it with, have improved the line tremendously in recent years. Increasing traffic is rewarding their efforts. For the first time for many years, small queues of boats may be seen working their way through Foxton locks—terrified novices, having their initiation into the glorious world of the canals, nervously poring over their instruction books, hardened boaters behind them fuming at the delay and using language which would have warmed the hearts of their spiritual ancestors, the men who worked the coal boats on the Leicester line run in the good days before the railways came and spoilt it all.

And at this point, with the comforting thought that at least the Union canals have more well wishers today than even in the spacious days of the Praeds, we must leave the story of these two unlucky, adorable canals. It is to be hoped that, whether or not they succeed in turning their losses into gain, they will be kept and treasured as priceless, irreplaceable amenities whose value to the community—to walkers and anglers, naturalists and artists, as much as to boaters—increases yearly as the sanities of life retreat before the irresistible march of the forces of Mammon, miscalled progress. Were they to go, the landscape of the Shires, the heart of England at its most English, would be impoverished beyond measure, and I for one would not wish to know it.

Notes

As extensive use has been made of the minutes of the Leicestershire & Northamptonshire Union, Grand Union and Grand Junction Canal companies, references to them have only been quoted to cover important points. Where no reference is given for a statement in the text, it will normally have been based on one of these sources.

NOTES TO CHAPTER 1 (*pages* 14–46)

The Leicestershire & Northamptonshire Union Canal, 1792–1809

1. British Transport Historical Records, LNC 1/1, 19 March 1792; *Leicester Journal*, 23 March 1792.
2. *Leicester Herald*, 5 May 1792.
3. *LJ*, 11 May 1792.
4. *LJ*, 18 May 1792.
5. *LH*, 19 May 1792.
6. *LH*, 12 May 1792.
7. *LJ*, 25 May 1792; *LH*, 26 May 1792.
8. *LH*, 2 June 1792.
9. BTHR, LNC 1/1, 27 June 1792; *LJ*, 29 June 1792; *LH*, 30 June 1792.
10. Northamptonshire County Record Office, 1C 2828; *LJ*, 10 August 1792; *LH*, 11 August 1792.
11. BTHR, LNC 1/1, 6 August 1792.
12. *LH*, 18 August 1792.
13. *LJ*, 14 September 1792.
14. *LH*, 22 September 1792.
15. *LH*, 3 November 1792.
16. *LJ*, 12 October 1792.
17. *LJ*, 12 October 1792.
18. *LH*, 3 November 1792.
19. *LJ*, 7 December 1792.
20. Pamphlet, *Reasons offered to the consideration of Parliament why they should not grant their immediate consent to the petition of the Committee of the Union Canal from Leicester by Harborough to Northampton* (1793). Leicester City Reference Library, Pamphlets 83.
21. *Northampton Merucry*, 16 February 1793.
22. *LH*, 2 March 1793.
23. *LH*, 16 March 1793.
24. House of Lords Record Office: Proceedings of Committees on Unopposed Private Bills, 28 March 1793.
25. *LH*, 4 May 1793.
26. *LH*, 11 May 1793.
27. *LJ*, 10 May 1793.

28. Chinnery, G. A., *Records of the Borough of Leicester*, vol V, (1967), pp 520, 547.
29. *LH*, 13 July 1793.
30. *Northampton Mercury*, 22 June 1793.
31. Hadfield, Charles, *Canals of the East Midlands* (2nd edn, 1970), pp 35, 40
32. Chinnery, p 284.
33. *Northampton Mercury*, 8 June 1793.
34. *LH*, 30 November 1793.
35. *LH*, 21 December 1793.
36. *LH*, 30 November 1793.
37. *LH*, 21 December 1793.
38. *LH*, 8 February 1794.
39. *LH*, 15 February 1794.
40. *LJ*, 14 February 1794.
41. *LH*, 15 February 1794.
42. *LJ*, 5 April 1794.
43. *LJ*, 18 April 1794.
44. *LJ*, 5 May 1794.
45. BTHR, LNC 1/2, 30 April 1794.
46. *LJ*, 19 September 1794.
47. BTHR, LNC 1/2, 27 November 1794; *LH*, 5 December 1794.
48. *LH*, 15 December 1794.
49. *LJ*, 31 October 1794.
50. *LH*, 3 April 1795; *LJ*, 3 April 1795.
51. *LJ*, 2 November 1795.
52. *LJ*, 2 November 1795.
53. BTHR, LNC 1/2, 6 July 1796.
54. BTHR, LNC 1/2, 10 August 1796.
55. BTHR, LNC 1/2, 25 January 1797.
56. *LJ*, 21 April 1797.
57. *LJ*, 9 August 1799.
58. Leicestershire County Record Office, QS 50/1/1.
59. *LJ*, 7 May 1802.
60. Pamphlet, *Report by James Barnes on the Works on the Leicestershire and Northamptonshire Union Canal* (1802): Library of the Institution of Civil Engineers, Tracts 4to, vol 7 (Canals).
61. Pamphlet, *A Survey and Report of the Proposed Extension of the Union Canal from Gumley Wharf, in Leicestershire, to the Grand Junction Canal, near Buckby-Wharf in Northamptonshire, made by Order of the Committee of the Union Canal Company. By Thomas Telford, Civil Engineer, FRS Edin.* (1803): Library of the Institution of Civil Engineers, Tracts 4to, vol 7 (Canals).
62. *LJ*, 20 June 1803.
63. Northants County Record Office, 1L 2451a.
64. Northants County Record Office, 1L 2451a.
65. *LJ*, 5 November 1804
66. House of Lords Record Office: *Plan of a Proposed Extension of the Union Canal from Dibdale* (sic) *Wharf to Market Harborough in the County of Leicester* (1805).
67. House of Lords Record Office: Proceedings of Committees on Unopposed Bills, 20 June 1805.
68. Leicestershire County Record Office QS 79/3/14.
69. *LJ*, 9 September 1809.

70. *LJ*, 3 June 1808.
71. *LJ*, 20 October 1809.

NOTES TO CHAPTER 2 (*pages* 14–78)

The Grand Union Canal, 1804–14

1. BTHR, LNC 1/9, 30 May 1808.
2. *LJ*, 3 June 1808.
3. *LH*, 3 November 1792.
4. Northants County Record Office, 1L 2451a/2.
5. *LJ*, 9 September 1808.
6. *LJ*, 9 September 1808, 16 September 1808.
7. Leics CRO, QS 72/11; Northants CRO CP 12.
8. *LJ*, 12 January 1810.
9. *Northampton Mercury*, 27 January 1810.
10. *Northampton Mercury*, 10 March 1810.
11. *Northampton Mercury*, 28 April 1810.
12. House of Lords Record Office, Deposited Plan, 1810.
13. House of Lords Record Office: Proceedings of Committees on Unopposed Private Bills, 22 May 1810.
14. BTHR, GUC 1/2, 13 December 1810.
15. *Northampton Mercury*, 1 December 1810.
16. BTHR, GUC 1/2, 11 April 1811.
17. BTHR, GUC 1/2, 12 September 1811.
18. BTHR, GUC 1/2, 12 December 1811.
19. BTHR, GUC 1/2, 6 February 1812.
20. BTHR, GUC 1/2, 3 June 1812.
21. BTHR, GUC 1/8, 18 September 1812.
22. BTHR, GUC 1/2, 28 October 1812.
23. Waterways Museum, Engineer's Plan and Section, BW453.
24. Northants CRO, 1L 2451a, 1L 2446, 1L 2447.
25. BTHR, GUC 1/2, 9 October 1813.
26. BTHR, GUC 1/2, 9 October 1813.
27. Waterways Museum, Engineer's Plan and Section, BW453.
28. BTHR, GUC 1/2, 3 November 1813.
29. Waterways Museum, Engineer's Plan and Section, BW453.
30. *LJ*, 12 August 1814.
31. BTHR, GUC 1/2, 7 September 1814.

NOTES TO CHAPTER 3 (*pages* 79–103)

The Old Union Canal, 1809–63)

1. *LJ*, 22 December 1809.
2. *Northampton Mercury*, 20 January 1810.
3. *LJ*, 20 April 1810.
4. *LJ*, 9 November 1810; 6 March 1812.
5. *LJ*, 26 July 1811.
6. BTHR, LNC 1/9, 16 November 1812.
7. *LJ*, 2 July 1813.

8. BTHR, LNC 1/9, 21 November 1814.
9. *LJ*, 12 August 1814.
10. BTHR, LNC 1/9, 18 May 1818; 16 November 1818.
11. BTHR, LNC 1/9, 17 May 1841.
12. BTHR, LNC 1/4, 4 December 1849.
13. BTHR, GUC 1/11, 20 July 1849.
14. BTHR, LNC 1/4, 15 October 1847.
15. BTHR, LNC 1/4, 14 April 1848, 13 May 1848.
16. BTHR, LNC 1/5, 9 April 1858.
17. *LJ*, 15 September 1809.
18. *LJ*, 6 October 1809.
19. *Northampton Mercury*, 13 January 1810.
20. *LJ*, 9 March 1810.
21. *LJ*, 7 September 1810.
22. *LJ*, 7 September 1810.
23. *LJ*, 23 November 1810.
24. *LJ*, 30 November 1810.
25. *LJ*, 14 December 1810; BTHR LNC 1/9, 19 December 1810.
26. Northants CRO, 72 7128.
27. *LJ*, 24 June 1814.
28. *Leicester Chronicle*, 17 February 1838.

NOTES TO CHAPTER 4 (*pages* 106–134)

The Grand Union Canal, 1814–63

1. BTHR, GUC 1/7, 1 June 1863, 8 June 1863.
2. BTHR, GUC 1/2, 1 December 1815.
3. BTHR, GUC 1/6, 4 June 1827.
4. BTHR, GUC 1/2, 7 July 1837.
5. BTHR, GUC 1/2, 1 February 1815.
6. *LJ*, 6 January 1815; BTHR, GUC 1/2, 18 January 1815.
7. BTHR, GUC 1/10, 17 April 1822.
8. BTHR, GUC 1/10, 17 July 1822.
9. BTHR, GUC 1/10, 25 January 1833, 3 May 1833.
10. BTHR, GUC 1/11, 28 July 1847.
11. BTHR, GUC 1/2, 14 March 1821.
12. BTHR, GUC 1/2, 17 July 1836.
13. BTHR, GUC 1/10, 6 January 1837.
14. BTHR, GUC 1/2, 31 May 1834.
15. BTHR, GUC 1/2, 9 June 1834.
16. BTHR, GUC 1/10, 30 July 1834, 27 October 1834.
17. BTHR, GUC 1/2, 17 August 1836.
18. Leics CRO, QS 73/100/11/45; BTHR GUC 1/11, 21 May 1847, 9 July 1847.
19. BTHR, GUC 1/11, 5 January 1847.
20. BTHR, GUC 1/12, 1 September 1854.
21. BTHR, GUC 1/7, 4 November 1861.
22. BTHR, GUC 1/12, 31 October 1862.
23. BTHR, GUC 1/12, 11 December 1862; *Leicester Chronicle*, 13 December 1862.

NOTES TO CHAPTER 5 (*pages* 138–160)

The Union Canals, 1863–94

1. BTHR, LNC 1/6, 17 December 1867.
2. BTHR, LNC 1/8, 16 February 1887; GUC 1/4, 16 February 1887.
3. BTHR, LNC 1/8, 28 September 1887.
4. BTHR, LNC 1/10, 16 May 1864.
5. BTHR, LNC 1/6, 30 July 1873, 14 August 1873, 13 November 1873.
6. BTHR, GUC 1/12, 3 December 1864.
7. BTHR, GUC 1/4, 6 November 1882.
8. BTHR, GUC 1/4, 14 September 1883.
9. BTHR, GUC 1/4, 12 October 1883.
10. BTHR, GUC 1/4, 10 July 1885.
11. BTHR, GUC 1/2, 4 June 1866.
12. *LJ*, 25 August 1865, 1 September 1865; *Leicester Chronicle*, 26 August 1865, 9 September 1865.
13. BTHR, LNC 1/10, 20 November 1865.
14. BTHR, GUC 1/2, 31 May 1867.
15. BTHR, GUC 1/2, 30 October 1867.
16. BTHR, GUC 1/2, 4 November 1867.
17. BTHR, GUC 1/2, 14 November 1869, 17 February 1870.
18. BTHR, GUC 1/3, 26 July 1879.
19. BTHR, GUC 1/4, 15 February 1888.
20. J. Storey, *Historical Sketch of some of the principal Works and Undertakings of the Council of the Borough of Leicester* (1895).
21. Leicester City Reference Library, Pamphlets 62, 03, vol 6.
22. BTHR, LNC 1/10, 18 May 1874.
23. Leicester City Reference Library, Pamphlets 82, 04, vol 2.
24. Leicester City Reference Library, Pamphlets 62, 03, vol 6.
25. Leicester City Museum: Minutes of the Flood Works Committee of the Borough Council, 19 January 1881.
26. Flood Works Committee minutes, 7 June 1886.
27. Flood Works Committee minutes, 18 July 1888.
28. Returns to the Board of Trade in respect of the Railway and Canal Traffic Act 1888; Flood Works Committee minutes, 19 February 1890.
29. BTHR, LNC 1/10, 19 May 1890.
30. BTHR, LNC 1/10, 15 May 1882.
31. BTHR, LNC 1/5, 18 September 1863, 2 October 1863, 9 October 1863.
32. BTHR LNC 1/8, 16 March 1892.
33. BTHR, GJC 1/24, 13 April 1892.
34. BTHR, GJC 1/24, 10 May 1893.
35. BTHR, LNC 1/8, 30 May 1893.
36. BTHR, LNC 1/8, 21 June 1893.
37. BTHR, GJC 1/24, 12 July 1893.

NOTES TO CHAPTER 6 (*pages* 162–180)

The Grand Junction Regime, 1894–1929

1. BTHR, MT 1/22.
2. BTHR, GJC 1/25, 12 May 1897.

3. BTHR, GJC 1/26, 8 October 1902.
4. BTHR, GJC 1/26, 14 October 1903.
5. Waterways Museum.
6. BTHR, GJC 1/25, 14 July 1897.
7. Waterways Museum.
8. *Engineering*, 25 January 1901.
9. Pamphlet, *The "Thomas" Lift* (nd, prob 1906), in Leics CRO (DE 215/7) and Waterways Museum (W/D/63/45).
10. Waterways Museum.
11. BTHR, GJC 1/26, 11 April 1900.
12. BTHR, GJC 1/26, 8 August 1900.
13. Waterways Museum: Photographic Record of Works, Northern District of the Grand Junction Canal.
14. BTHR, GJC 1/26, 9 April 1902.
15. BTHR, GJC 1/28, 12 February 1913.
16. BTHR, GJC 1/29, 10 October 1917.
17. BTHR, GJC 1/47, 11 April 1928.
18. BTHR, GJC 1/28, 12 April 1911.

NOTES TO CHAPTER 7 (*pages* 184–187)

Trends, 1929–1971

1. Hadfield, Charles, *Canals of the East Midlands* (2nd edn, 1970), pp 240–1.
2. Rolt, L. T. C., *Narrow Boat* (2nd edn, 1948), pp 68–80.
3. Woolfitt, Susan, *Idle Women* (1947), pp 198–209.
4. Board of Survey of Canals and Waterways: Report (1955), p 68.
5. Board of Survey of Canals and Waterways: Report, p 69.
6. *Leicester Mercury*, 18 May 1964.
7. British Waterways Board: *The Future of the Waterways* (1964), p 35.
8. British Waterways Board, *The Future of the Waterways*, p 40.
9. British Waterways Board: *Facts about the Waterways* (1965), p 75.
10. *LJ*, 25 August 1797; *Leicester Chronicle*, 2 July 1831.

Bibliography

Hadfield, Charles. *The Canals of the East Midlands* (2nd edn, 1970)

Old Union Canals Society. *The 'Old Union' Canals of Leicestershire and Northamptonshire* (2nd edn, 1970)

Paterson, E. T. 'The Making of the Leicestershire Canals' (*Transactions of the Leicestershire Archaeological Society*, XXVII) (1951)

Priestley, J. *Historical Account of the Navigable Rivers, Canals and Railways throughout Great Britain* (1831)

Rolt, L. T. C. *Narrow Boat* (1944)

Salis, H. de. *Bradshaw's Canals and Navigable Rivers of England and Wales* (1904, reprinted 1969)

Woolfitt, S. *Idle Women* (1947)

Author's Acknowledgements

ONE of the many pleasures of research is experiencing the real kindness and willingness to help offered by those fortunate beings entrusted with the care of historical records. I have bothered many people in my delving into the past of the Union canals, and have invariably met with enthusiastic interest and co-operation. Among these good friends, I must first name Mr E. H. Fowkes and his staff at the British Transport Historical Records Office; I have leaned heavily upon the records preserved at their transport historian's paradise in Porchester Road. The staff of the House of Lords Record Office courteously gave me access to documents and plans relating to the formation of the Unions and their demise as independent units. In the territory of the canals, the archivists and their staffs at both the Leicestershire and the Northamptonshire Record Offices proved most helpful, producing quite unexpected documents from private collections deposited with them as well as those I was anticipating finding there. The Director and the Keeper of Archives at Leicester Museum kindly allowed me access to the records of the Borough Council relating to the Flood Prevention Schemes of the latter half of the nineteenth century, which, by dovetailing with the LNU minutes, for once presented me with both sides of the picture. The City Librarian of Leicester generously gave me free access to the files of the local newspapers extending back to the LNU's earliest days, and these proved quite indispensible in studying the origins of the canal.

At the Waterways Museum, Mr C. N. Hadlow, the former curator, was as helpful as always. His successor, Mr R. Hutchings, made me very welcome, and made available to me invaluable material which altered many of my preconceived ideas of my subjects' history; from nobody did I receive more willing help and kindness—and this is saying a very great deal.

Of the private sources I consulted, the Old Union Canals Society did more for me than I am sure they know—apart from publishing a booklet which every visitor to the canals, whether by boat or on foot, should carry with him. In particular, I may name the present Secretary, Mr J. Pyper, and Mr Malcolm Bower. My fellow members of the Railway & Canal Historical Society also proved, as usual, always ready to pass on information, often dug out laboriously with considerable trouble, with the lack of selfishness characteristic of them. They will, I know, accept a blanket word of thanks from me. I must, however, single out Mr Alan Faulkner, whose painstaking research on that formidable undertaking, the Grand Junction Canal, produced results which were placed at my disposal without hesitation; I trust that when Alan's book on the GJ appears, my own work will be a worthy tributary to it.

I was fortunate in being able to call on the knowledge of two gentlemen over special subjects. Mr P. Gardiner, of the Leicester Polytechnic, has made a special and highly detailed study of that fascinating phenomenon, the Foxton lift, in the course of which he has brought to light much new information. He most kindly made the fruits of his work—which I sincerely hope will appear in print—available to me, and discussed the technicalities of the lift with me to such good effect that, as the least mechanically minded of mortals, I hope that there are no howlers in my section relating to it. Mr D. S. Hunt, of Messrs Owston & Co, gave me a good deal of information about that interesting figure, Hiram Abiff Owston, Clerk to both companies for the last three decades or so of their independent lives.

On another special topic, the proposed extensions of the LNU from Debdale, I was greatly helped by the Librarian of the Institution of Civil Engineers, who permitted me to work on the reports by Barnes and Telford preserved in that library.

Leicester Museums courteously supplied the aerial photographs, the Waterways Museum those of Foxton lift, and the National Reference Library of Science and Invention the print of the patent specification. The rest are my own; I hope they will convey something of the ethos of those enchanting canals.

My last acknowledgement shall be to the two people to whom this books owes most—for without them, I doubt whether it would have been written. It was Charles Hadfield, doyen of canal historians and undisputed leader in the field, who found me in Porchester Road browsing through an Old Union minute book, and suggested that I might put my nose to the grindstone (he was actually more tactful than that) and work my researches into a book; otherwise, being far fonder of researching than recording, I might have gone on for years with no thought of publication. I hope he will not regret it. It has been a great comfort to me to have his advice always readily available.

Last of all, I must admit that the author's expressions of gratitude to his wife are not merely moral conscience-money for being allowed to vanish for days and evenings researching in the field and in the record office. There is no pleasure in life like research, but I imagine that most workers have fits of discouragement—when figures taken from different sources contradict one another, when important links in the chain of evidence are missing, when one's head aches after eight hours poring over crabbed Victorian handwriting, and a three-hour journey home. I certainly had, and my wife's unfailing support invariably cheered me up and sent me back for more. I discussed the book with her at every stage, and always found her advice invaluable; and we have spent much of our spare time on field work, from West Bridge to Norton. To crown it all, she produced the maps, a task far beyond me. I hope she will believe that I am truly grateful.

From all these good people I have received nothing but help and kindness; and I hope that any errors the book may contain—and what book contains none?—will be attributed entirely to my misreading of information, and not to those from whom I received it.

APPENDIX 1

LNU Receipts, Expenditure, and Dividends

Year	Receipts £	Expenditure £	Dividend £	s	d	
1806	1,153	7,981	—			
1807	1,890	11,947	—			
1808	2,065	13,512	—			
1809	4,246	11,313	—			
1810	2,394*	3,512*	—			
1811	3,000*	1,825*	—			
1812	8,506	4,600	—			
1813	6,524	4,391	2	0	0	
1814	7,698	4,875	2	0	0	
1815	9,585	4,164	2	0	0	
1816	10,851	3,759	4	0	0	
1817	8,960	3,024	2	0	0	
1818	8,823	2,952	4	0	0	
1819	9,826	4,334	2	10	0	(£2.50)
1820	10,131	3,320	4	0	0	
1821	10,111	3,251	2	0	0	
1822	8,395	2,835	2	0	0	
1823	9,748	2,663	4	0	0	
1824	9,867	2,933	4	0	0	
1825	11,243	3,682	4	0	0	
1826	9,944	2,832	4	0	0	
1827	10,063	2,777	4	0	0	
1828	9,822	2,740	4	0	0	
1829	9,686	2,793	4	0	0	
1830	8,624	2,357	2	0	0	
1831	9,069	2,533	4	0	0	
1832	8,668	2,650	4	0	0	
1833	9,242	3,099	2	0	0	
1834	9,997	2,818	4	0	0	
1835	11,475	2,957	4	5	0	(£4.25)
1836	15,119	3,263	5	0	0	
1837	15,682	3,609	6	0	0	
1838	13,554	3,595	6	0	0	
1839	13,499	2,370	5	15	0	(£4.75)
1840	12,404	2,455	5	0	0	
1841	12,023	2,929	4	15	0	(£4.75)
1842	11,680	2,978	4	10	0	(£4.50)
1843	11,253	2,702	4	0	0	
1844	12,249	2,804	4	10	0	(£4.50)
1845	12,752	2,742	4	15	0	(£4.75)
1846	11,642	2,787	4	15	0	(£4.75)
1847	13,161	2,606	5	10	0	(£5.50)

Year	Receipts £	Expenditure £	Dividend £	s	d	
1848	11,155	2,706	4	10	0	(£4.50)
1849	10,946	2,589	4	0	0	
1850	9,382	2,505	3	2	6	(£3.12½)
1851	6,874	2,184	2	7	6	(£2.37½)
1852	6,804	2,020	2	7	6	(£2.37½)
1853	7,157	2,041	2	10	0	(£2.50)
1854	6,513	2,218	2	5	0	(£2.25)
1855	5,684	2,213	2	0	0	
1856	5,166	2,098	1	12	6	(£1.62½)
1857	4,584	2,078	1	5	0	(£1.25)
1858	3,411	1,665	1	0	0	
1859	3,180	1,467		18	6	(92½p)
1860	3,452	1,565	1	0	0	
1861	2,820	1,484		17	6	(87½p)
1862	2,813	1,480		15	0	(75p)
1863	2,832	1,405		15	0	(75p)
1864	2,837	1,471		15	0	(75p)
1865	2,760	1,427		15	0	(75p)
1866	2,889	1,407		15	0	(75p)
1867	2,604	1,379		13	0	(65p)
1868	2,612	1,434		12	0	(60p)
1869	2,754	1,492		12	0	(60p)
1870	2,439	1,404		11	0	(55p)
1871	2,209	1,267		10	0	(50p)
1872	2,057	1,259		8	6	(42½p)
1873	1,910	1,048		9	0	(45p)
1874	1,965	1,100		9	0	(45p)
1875	1,954	1,058		9	0	(45p)
1876	1,894	1,097		8	0	(40p)
1877	1,912	1,024		8	9	(44p)
1878	1,954	1,109		8	9	(44p)
1879	1,782	1,026		7	10	(39p)
1880	1,901	1,095		8	6	(42½p)
1881	1,834	1,064		7	3	(36p)
1882	1,837	1,010		9	0	(45p)
1883	1,988	978		9	0	(45p)
1884	2,024	1,058		9	6	(47½p)
1885	1,836	1,017		9	0	(45p)
1886	1,849	1,083		7	6	(37½p)
1887	1,976	1,085		8	0	(40p)
1888	1,882	1,073		9	0	(45p)
1889	1,883	1,170		8	0	(40p)
1890	1,922	1,112		8	6	(42½p)
1891	1,916	1,121		8	0	(40p)
1892	1,786	981		8	6	(42½p)
1893	1,777	1,003		8	6	(42½p)
1894*	884	471		4	0	(20p)

* Half year only

GU Receipts, Expenditure, and Dividends 1808-94

(a) EXPENDITURE AND DIVIDENDS, 1808–62

Year	Expenditure £	Dividend £	s	d	Year	Expenditure £	Dividend £	s	d
1810	11,759 (includes all expenditure from 30 June 1808)				1829	2,193	1	0	0
					1830	3,664	1	0	0
					1831	3,136	1	0	0
1811	45,017				1832	2,881	1	0	0
1812	82,341				1833	3,046	1	0	0
1813	92,628				1834	5,274	—		
1814	63,265				1835	5,119	1	0	0
1815	18,623				1836	6,260	1	0	0
1816	8,323				1837	12,591	1	0	0
1817	5,272				1838	7,866	1	0	0
1818	6,443				1839	6,246	1	0	0
1819	5,345				1840	5,457	1	15	0 (£1.75)
1820	5,958				1841	6,565	1	15	0 (£1.75)
1821	5,509				1842	2,217	1	10	0 (£1.50)
1822	6,472				1843	2,187	1	10	0 (£1.50)
1823	5,569				1844	2,249	1	10	0 (£1.50)
1824	3,319				1845	2,252	2	0	0
1825	7,581				1846	2,272	2	0	0
1826	5,743				1847	2,497	2	0	0
1827	3,763	1	0	0	1848	2,248	1	15	0 (£1.75)
1828	3,943	1	0	0	1849	2,203	1	12	6 (£1.62½)

Year	Expenditure	Dividend			Year	Expenditure	Dividend		
	£	£	s	d		£	£	s	d
1850	2,272	1	10	0 (£1.50)	1857	2,299		15	6 (77½p)
1851	2,934	1	0	0	1858	2,735		13	0 (65p)
1852	1,944	1	0	0	1859	1,913		10	0 (50p)
1853	2,205	1	0	0	1860	1,853		10	0 (50p)
1854	2,117	1	0	0	1861	1,722		8	0 (40p)
1855	2,402		12	6 (62½p)	1862	1,171		7	0 (35p)
1856	2,216		15	0 (75p)					

(b) RECEIPTS, EXPENDITURE, AND DIVIDENDS, 1863–94

Year	Receipts	Expenditure	Dividend			Year	Receipts	Expenditure	Dividend		
	£	£	£	s	d		£	£	£	s	d
1863	1,333*	605*		9	0 (45p)	1879	1,491	993		3	6 (17½p)
1864	1,603*	548*		12	0 (60p)	1880	1,534	1,038		3	6 (17½p)
1865	2,633	1,109		10	0 (50p)	1881	1,302	1,253		—	
1866	2,723	1,129		9	0 (45p)	1882	1,506	1,057		2	3 (11p)
1867	2,458	1,284		4	0 (20p)	1883	1,499	1,160		1	3 (6p)
1868	2,521	1,242		6	0 (30p)	1884	1,414	1,081		1	6 (7½p)
1869	2,427	1,465		6	0 (30p)	1885	1,380	1,071		1	0 (5p)
1870	2,344	1,365		6	0 (30p)	1886	1,670	1,278		1	3 (6p)
1871	1,855	1,346		4	0 (20p)	1887	1,306	1,051		1	0 (5p)
1872	1,812	1,154		4	6 (22½p)	1888	1,514	1,006		2	0 (10p)
1873	1,569	1,012		4	0 (20p)	1889	1,541	1,094		2	0 (10p)
1874	1,573	1,072		3	6 (17½p)	1890	1,492	1,087		2	0 (10p)
1875	1,397	997		2	10 (14p)	1891	1,497	1,079		2	0 (10p)
1876	1,410	1,026		2	9 (14p)	1892	1,336	994		2	0 (10p)
1877	1,528	999		3	9 (19p)	1893	1,306	949		2	3 (11p)
1878	1,527	1,000		3	8 (18½p)	1894	630*	470*		1	0* (5p)

APPENDIX 3

Tonnage through Foxton, 1905-30

Year	*Tons*	*Year*	*Tons*
1905	33,425	1918	10,385
1906	36,309	1919	12,857
1907	31,417	1920	12,824
1908	31,540	1921	8,238
1909	39,711	1922	11,037
1910	40,767	1923	7,570
1911	41,520	1924	9,917
1912	37,258	1925	12,314
1913	36,662	1926	9,728
1914	34,910	1927	9,994
1915	23,519	1928	9,676
1916	15,482	1929	7,216
1917	16,713	1930	5,806 (to October only)

APPENDIX 4

Table of distances on the Leicester Line

(Taken from T. W. Millner's Survey, made in 1895)

Distance *miles*	*yd*	*Place*
0	0	Norton Junction
1	510	Welton landing
1	1,254	Watford wharf
1	1,370	Welton Station wharf
2	354½	Watford Bottom Lock
2	711¼	Watford Top Lock
3	1,364½	Crick tunnel—south end
4	1,132¼	Crick tunnel—north end
4	1,620½	Crick wharf
7	385	Yelvertoft wharf
7	1,634¼	Winwick landing
10	739¼	Elkington landing
15	946	Welford branch
16	503¾	North Kilworth wharf
17	153	Bosworth tunnel—south end
17	1,323½	Bosworth tunnel—north end
17	1,413½	Bosworth landing
21	1,309	Lubenham landing
22	1,683	Foxton Top Lock
23	196½	Foxton Bottom Lock
23	231	Market Harborough branch
24	511½	Debdale wharf
25	831¼	Gumley landing
26	387¾	Saddington reservoir feeder
26	492½	Smeeton aqueduct
26	1,471	Saddington tunnel—south end

Distance miles	yd	Place
27	592	Saddington tunnel—north end
28	310	Kibworth Top Lock
29	748	Great Glenn aqueduct
31	24	Newton Harcourt landing
32	1,660¼	Kilby Bridge wharf
34	1,067¾	Wigston Magna Ironworks landing
35	1,656	Blaby wharf
36	1,540	Glen Parva landing
38	848½	Junction with River Soar
38	1,608	Aylestone landing
39	1,611½	St Mary's landing
40	482½	New Lock
40	660	Leicester Corporation public wharf
40	1,452	Leicester Corporation public wharf
41	244¼	West Bridge, Leicester
41	388¾	Termination of canal

WELFORD BRANCH

miles	yd	Place
0	0	Junction with main line, Husbands Bosworth
1	405¾	Lock
1	670	Termination of branch, Welford wharf

MARKET HARBOROUGH BRANCH

miles	yd	Place
0	0	Junction with main line, Foxton
0	880	Foxton landing
0	1,002¼	Foxton wharf
2	99	Gallow Hill landing
2	180½	Gallow Hill bone mill
5	895¼	Termination of Union wharf, Market Harborough, and of branch

APPENDIX 5

Locks

Distance from Norton Junction miles	yd	GJ No	LNU No	Name	Fall
2	354½	1–7		Watford flight	53ft*
22	1,683	8–17		Foxton flight	75ft*
28	310	18	24	Kibworth Top	26ft 10in (Kibworth Top to Kibworth Bottom)
28	759¼	19	23	Kibworth Second	
28	946½	20	22	Taylor's Turnover	
28	1,135	21	21	Kibworth Bottom	
29	182	22	20	Crane's	4ft 11in
30	1,342¾	23	29	Newton Top	6ft 3in
30	1,689¼	24	18	Newton Middle	7ft 6in
31	250¼	25	17	Newton Bottom	7ft 8in
31	1,181½	26	16	Bottom Half Mile	29ft 6in (Bottom Half Mile to Bumble Bee)
31	1,298½	27	15	Turnover	
31	1,708	28	14	Langham's (Tythorn)	
32	310	29	13	Bumble Bee	
33	516½	30	12	Kilby Bridge	6ft 2in
33	1,140¾	31	11	Double Rail	7ft 6in
34	277½	32	10	Erving's	7ft 1in
34	1,565	33	9	Bush	7ft 4in
35	1,339½	34	8	Dunn's (Little Glen)	5ft 10in
36	359½	35	7	Whetstone Lane	6ft
37	65¾	36	6	Gee's	7ft 4in
37	785½	37	5	Blue Bank	7ft 9in
38	573¼	38	4	King's	7ft 8in
39	467	39	3	Aylestone Mill	4ft 10in
39	1,692¼	40	2	St Mary's Mill	3ft 2in
40	482½	41	1	New (Toll House)	7ft 6in

No 41 (New Lock) replaced Swans Mill Lock and Castle Mill Lock, each of which had a fall of 3ft.

LNU locks were 74ft long by 15ft wide, with 5ft depth of water on the cill.

GU locks were 74ft 3in long by 7ft 3in wide, with 5ft depth of water on the cill.

* Successive owners of Foxton and Watford flights have given different figures for their fall. The old GU gave 75ft and 55ft respectively; the GJ 75ft 2in and 53ft; the new GU 74ft 7in and 54ft 7in; and British Waterways 75ft and 52ft 6in.

Index